Donna Lee
1990

FOUR CORNERS ON MAIN STREET

FOUR CORNERS ON MAIN STREET

A novel by PAUL ROSS

Somerville House Publishing
Toronto

Canadian Cataloguing in Publication Data

Ross, Paul, 1933-
Four corners on Main Street

ISBN 0-921051-33-6

I. Title.

PS8585.077F68 1990 C813′.54 C90-093343-4
PR9199.2.R68F68 1990

Printed in Canada

Design: Andrew Smith
Cover art: Douglas Fraser
Author photograph: Colleen Maguire

Published by Somerville House Publishing,
a division of Somerville House Books Ltd.,
1 Eglinton Avenue East,
Toronto, Ontario, Canada
M4P 3A1

To my wife,
the electric Heather Joy.
And to my kids,
the wonderous Tegan and the mighty Quinn.

Thanks to Florence Rosberg who, next to her family, loves the written word best. And to Alice Munro, Jack Batten, Patrick Crean and Jack McClelland.

FOUR CORNERS ON MAIN STREET

CHAPTER ONE

MY WIFE, FAITH, AND I HAVE TAKEN MARRIAGE COUNSELLING. Why not? No one tells you anything before you're married.

Once during a wedding ceremony I asked a doctor, who was also a guest, if she was happily married. She whispered, "No!"

I asked her why she seemed so happy at this one. She said, "One always hopes it will work out for the next couple."

It rarely does. . . . Crazy, eh?

Anyhow, Faith and I were committed to ten one-hour sessions. The counsellor happened to be a psychiatrist from Stratford, Ontario. In our first interview she told us that at the end of ten sessions we would know one of two things. The two things were:

Whether we could make the marriage work.
Whether we couldn't make the marriage work.

It seemed reasonable.

By the end of the sessions Faith and I knew the secret. This is not to say we didn't die a little inside on our way to the secret. Discussing relationships with your spouse is never easy. Add a psychiatrist and I guarantee real torment.

I know, I know ... you want the secret ... right?. . . And preferably without the stomach cramps. . . . To tell you the truth, I'm not so sure it will help . . . I mean if you don't get sick, even a little. But for what it's worth, here you go. . . . All you need are the answers to three magic questions.

When you married your spouse:

What did you think you were getting?

What in fact did you end up with?

Can you live with what you got?

Simple, huh?

The psychiatrist said that one in ten marriages was happy. Do me a favour: if you know of even two, drop me a line, OK?

Having admitted all this, I don't suppose you'll be too impressed when I tell you that I have a Ph.D. in social work. If I don't know about marriage, who does? . . . Wait till I tell you what Faith does. She's a lawyer, specializing in family law. . . . Nobody has all the answers!

*

Faith and I live in Yelton, a small town of about three thousand and seven hundred people, located in Southwestern Ontario. We met at university, in Saskatchewan. We have no kids and no pets; I'd like to have kids. Faith says the world doesn't deserve our kids yet. She may be right about that.

*

Iva Blyth lives in Yelton too. She has a store, IVA'S STATIONERY, located at the four corners. The four corners form the one and only intersection in Yelton with traffic lights.

The four corners are also the roosting place for kids

with nothing to do. These are, of course, kids with long stringy hair, cigarette breath; young girls with stubby fingers, chipped nail polish, and tight jeans; youths in black leather jackets, failing teeth, and combs jammed into their back seat pockets. Not a pretty sight, bunting and pushing, swearing and spitting right in front of Iva's entrance.

Iva asked Police Chief Shelton to do something about these strays . . . anything. Nothing happened. The kids still hung out, putting gum in her door lock, leaving empty beer cans and Pickin' Chicken boxes on her front step. Chief Shelton doesn't take female entrepreneurs seriously. In fact, in Yelton nobody takes women seriously . . . not even the women!

In spite of this attitude, Iva has done well. Her husband, Willard, died some seventeen years earlier, at the age of forty-seven. His liver had failed him despite his long association with Alcoholics Anonymous. It had been a very forgiving chapter. If only his liver had been as forgiving.

Iva had been running the store, more or less, for years, but after Willard's death she was unfettered and quickly added a Radio Shack franchise and recently video movie rentals. In the front of her shop she sold greeting cards, penny candy, stationery, lottery tickets, and magazines, from *Canadian Living* to a porn magazine called *High Society*. In the back she sold electronics. Iva liked to say she sold everything from *High Society* to high fidelity.

Police Chief Shelton liked to say that Iva had driven poor Willard to an early grave. To the boys at Laurie's Light Lunch, the Chief said, "If Iva hadn't something to bitch about, she'd invent it." Chief Shelton also liked to say, "What Iva needs is a good screw." All the men at Laurie's agreed with the Chief as if they were just the guys to do it.

None of them, in fact, was the guy to do it. Iva had, years before, had her fill of erect penises. It had for the most part got her two boys, one of ambiguous sexual gender, currently enrolled in a library course at a community college, and the second, a roofer, following in his father's liquid wake.

Iva had more important matters to deal with . . . like the loafers who hung around her entrance. Finally, in desperation, Iva wrote to the Town Council, with a copy to the local newspaper. This is what her letter said:

DEAR MAYOR:

I want to complain (again) about the loafers who hang around my store on Main Street. They interfere with the people who try to pass on the sidewalk, especially older people who aren't used to boys wearing ear-rings, or girls wearing dirty slogans on their chests. The language is no hell either.

The other merchants are fed up too. The police just laugh at us if we complain. Chief Shelton says kids have got rights. Well, we got rights too.

It's no wonder the police never catch kids drinking beer and peeing in my doorway. Everyone in town knows the police go off duty at 2:00 A.M., or they see them coming in the police cruiser. Are these men policemen or what?

We want these kids off our street so old people can walk without being molested, and we can make a living.

Sincerely
Iva Blyth (Mrs.)
cc Yelton Beacon Harold

*

MAGIC QUESTION NUMBER ONE: *What did you think you were getting?*

I'll tell you what I didn't expect: that when Faith and I got married she'd get involved in this damn business with Iva Blyth, and that's for sure.

Faith was . . . twenty, fragile, vulnerable, and beautiful. She was Milton and Keats, Stendhal and Maugham, Beresford-Howe, Munro, and Laurence. Faith was a full skirt, an arm full of books, hugging them to her sky-blue angora sweater. She was sweet and gentle sex, Robert Altman movies, candelight dinners, The Moody Blues, Don McLean, and Harry Nilsson.

*

Faith says I'm full of shit. She says she never even owned a blue angora sweater. . . . She may be right about that too!

I'll tell you what else I didn't expect: that after fifteen years of marriage, at the age of forty, I'd be driving a hundred and twenty miles to the Royal York Hotel in Toronto to see José Feliciano. Faith, who sees herself as a child of the sixties, insisted we go to relive her past, as she remembered it.

Trust me: if you can't afford the $150 it cost for the night, consider yourself among the lucky. For one thing, the food was overpriced and awful. For another, they don't play instruments anymore. They operate deafening machines.

And picture this . . . at the curtain call, to mark her youth, as she remembered it, Faith stands up . . . alone

. . . in that huge, filled-to-capacity, goddamn room and gives José Feliciano a standing ovation. . . . I just hope someone told him after the show.

What did I think I was getting? I thought I was getting Leslie Caron, straight out of *An American in Paris*. I thought I was getting peace, warmth, refuge, a place to lay my head. I thought I was getting what I deserved.

*

Shel Shelton looked every inch a police chief. He was tall and muscular. He sported the full chief regalia, whether at an official function, such as directing traffic away from the cenotaph at Princess Anne Park on Remembrance Day, or just strolling down Main Street on a routine walkabout.

His wardrobe consisted of a chief's hat, complete with gold braid, like General MacArthur's, white shirt, double starch, and black pants, crisp crease, with an embroidered black silk ribbon running down the outseam. Yeltonites were suckers for a uniform. The Chief's bearing demanded respect. . . . Those who didn't know him, gave it.

His wife, Sheila, knew him . . . like a book. She knew he hated his job, suffered migraine headaches over it. Shelton had dreamed of becoming a sergeant of detectives while on the Toronto police force, but as the years passed and he remained in a police cruiser, he answered Yelton's ad in the *Toronto Sun*. The only other application had been from an alcoholic constable from a neighbouring municipality. The town fathers jumped at Shel Shelton.

Shelton had dreamed of big crime, instead he got Yelton. On a good month this is what the police occurrence sheet looked like:

OCCURRENCE: dog at large . . . taken to kennel.

OCCURRENCE: break and enter . . . report window forced at Van Baren warehouse. No entry.

OCCURRENCE: Highway Traffic Act . . . 2 charges, careless driving.
3 charges, unnecessary noise (tire squeal).

OCCURRENCE: Liquor Licence Act . . . 4 charges, open bottle in motor vehicle.
1 charge, serve liquor to minors.

And so on.

*

Shortly after his arrival Chief Shelton suffered his first migraine headache. He discovered to his horror that Yeltonites were, for the most part, law-abiding. How do you enforce the law against people who don't break it? How do you exercise authority when no one challenges it? . . . The Chief spent hours contemplating this problem.

* He convinced council to pass a by-law requiring the organizers of the local Santa Claus parade to apply to the police for a permit, after seventy-five years of holding parades without one.

* He prohibited car washing on Sundays.

* He banned sunbathing as well as infant nudity in Princess Anne Park.

* He prohibited kids from flying kites in town because of hydro lines.

* He ordered women to remove clothes-lines located in their backyards that were under fifteen feet off

the ground as a precaution against decapitation or strangulation.

The people of Yelton loved it. Here at last was an activist. Not only was the enforcement of law being done, it had the appearance of being done. Here was a police chief and a police force that gave value for money.

The Chief's headaches increased in severity and number. He decided to up the ante.

* He required . . . elderly inmates of any local senior citizens' home and/or nursing home to be accompanied by registered nurse, or registered nursing assistant, while abroad on the streets of Yelton. . . . The citizens went wild with appreciation.

* He sent word from his sick-bed that sidewalk traffic be one way on the north side of Main Street, and the opposite direction on the south side. The Chief reasoned that one-way traffic would protect children, the elderly, and the infirm from being trampled by younger and healthier oncoming pedestrians.

Everyone got into the spirit of the regulation, tacking up and down Main Street as the need to change direction dictated, so that pedestrians were always heading the same way, helping the old and the very young en route. . . .

The Chief received the news that he had been nominated as Yelton's Man of the Year from his darkened room.

*

MAGIC QUESTION NUMBER ONE (CONT'D): *What did you think you were getting?*

Faith told the marriage counsellor she thought I was

kind and caring. That's it, kind and caring. What the hell did that mean? . . . And who says I'm not?

*

My mother, Velma, is a kind and caring woman. I will say that about her. She believes in perfection . . . perfection and respect.

I grew up respecting Louis St.-Laurent and believing that Cary Grant and Leslie Caron were perfect. Not that everyone was perfect to Velma. She had no time, for example, for Nikita Khrushchev or Frank Sinatra. She did feel, however, that each could be redeemed. Perhaps it is her Catholic faith that gives her such hope. Perhaps her faith has also provided her with the ability to paint the world into two colours, black and white.

My father, Sidney, is Jewish. He worked as a sewing machine operator for forty-five years at Adelaide Fine Silks in Toronto, a company that manufactured ladies' undergarments. My dad swore the only silk that ever found its way into the shop covered the pudendum of Sophie Seligman, the head seamstress who had been screwing the boss for twenty-three years. Sidney thinks the whole world is a bunch of goniffs. Sidney has only one colour on his palette: black.

You might have thought, with two such divergent approaches to life, I'd have grown up schizophrenic. Not so. Early on I accepted my mother's humanist philosophy and, for the most part, rejected Sidney's as not particularly well thought out.

I will admit, however, on one occasion, at the airport in Denver, while waiting for a long-overdue connecting flight to Chicago, being tempted to engage a young man, representing Jews for Jesus, in a conversation.

I wanted to ask him whether Jews for Jesus kids got

out of school for both Jewish and Christian holidays. To this day I don't know. Good luck to them if they do!

*

Can I go back here, just a little? When I say I didn't learn anything from Sid, that's not exactly true, or fair. I did learn about terror.

My poor father's life has been filled with terror. As best as I can make out, my father has lived with terror every day of his life.

He was terrified that my mother was having an affair. With whom? Anyone. The milkman. One of her women friends. Even Jesus.

At work he was terrified that someone, anyone, was getting benefits not accorded him. He was even jealous of Sophie Seligman.

At budget time my father would pore through the papers, expecting at any moment to see his own name leap from the newspaper, announcing a special tax against him. The fact that they omitted his name didn't soften his belief that, in any case, this or that measure was aimed directly at him.

And God help the cop who stopped the line of traffic he happened to be in, or the waiter otherwise occupied. Each had singled out my father to shun and ignore. My father dreaded the humiliation and had as little contact with the world as possible.

I guess it would be fair to say that I did learn something from my father. I learned to smell the stench of terror from fifty feet.

Is it any wonder, then, that when I was nineteen one of my favourite authors was the much-vaunted philosopher Kierkegaard who, like my father, spent a whole lot of time worrying about dread?

Kierkegaard, as you probably know, suffered from profound depression, which is perhaps why he spent so much energy writing about terror. It may also explain why no one understands what the hell he was talking about.

Another reason I liked Kierkegaard was his intellectual interest in original sin. At age nineteen I was still a virgin and spent a fair bit of time thinking about original sin myself.

And the way that old depressive philosopher could spin terror and original sin together. You have to admire the man. This is more or less what I think he was trying to say:

> *Adam found himself in the Garden of Eden. He probably didn't know it was the Garden of Eden. To tell you the truth, Adam didn't know a heck of a lot about anything. You see, Adam was innocent—innocence back then was ignorance—and therefore ignorance was bliss.*
>
> *Then, for some reason never really made clear, God pointed out to Adam that there were apples on a particular tree that Adam was not to eat.*
>
> *You have to remember, up to this point Adam just sort of was. It wasn't a question of doing or not doing . . . decisions had already been taken! Suddenly (God knows why), He was saying to Adam, "Lookit, you can eat that apple, but personally I wouldn't advise it!"*
>
> *Oh . . . God . . .* CHOICE! *. . . Adam was terrified. Suddenly he had to make a* DECISION.
>
> *"Oh," Adam probably said, "I need this like a hole in the head. Should I try the apple? If I do, will it lead to something worse? . . . Like fooling around with women?". . . And there we have it . . . original sin.*

Kierkegaard reasoned from this abundance of evidence that it wasn't lust that caused the fall but CHOICE . . . man's awareness that he could tell the Lord to go to hell, and do whatever he wanted. This revelation, the discovery by Adam of choice (according to Kierkegaard), filled man with dread.

You think that's far-fetched? . . . You make decisions so easily?

*

Iva's letter landed on Mayor Smith's desk at the Town Hall. Dillman Smith was also a general insurance agent. Being Mayor of Yelton is a part-time job. Dillman Smith was an insurance man first.

It turned out that Dillman was also a natural politician. His political instincts, for the most part, were true. He confided to his wife, Susan, who wondered at his ability to avoid confrontation, that he was guided by an inner voice, a sensation, that went off in his head when called upon by him.

Dillman had first been visited by the voice some five years before. It advised him to run for the town's highest office. "Word has it," he had explained to Susan Smith, "that this is my time." The voice had not misled him. It was a year when civic complacency had reached an all-time high and nobody else was prepared to stand. Dillman's inner voice understood a sure thing. Word also had it that it was an opportunity for the salesman to meet more people in his official capacity as meeter and greeter. . . .

Not many people stand for public office because they care about sewers, streets, or tax-collecting, say what you will!

The Mayor was paid for each meeting or other town

function he attended. The more he attended, the more he received. The little voice urged Smith to keep up his attendance. Dillman never did miss a meeting, or an event, no matter how obscure. When questioned by a budget director alarmed at the Mayor's mounting stipend, and his planned attendance at the grand re-opening of Gord's Shoe and Leather Repair, Dillman whispered in confidence: "Word has it, I should be there."

The Mayor also got to attend conventions, at town expense, all over the province. Word had it that it gave him the chance to network with other public officials. It also gave him the chance to commit adultery. To the budget director, who complained about the Mayor's convention expenses, Smith liked to point out that he never took his wife.

*

MAGIC QUESTION NUMBER ONE (CONT'D):
What Faith thought she was getting.

I forgot to mention. Faith also said to our marriage counsellor that she thought I was cute.

In Yelton there was one piece of intelligence you could take to the bank, and that was this: the Mayor disliked the Chief of Police and the Chief of Police disliked the Mayor. In a small town there is only so much authority to go around.

*

When the Mayor finished reading Iva's letter (cc The Yelton Beacon Harold), he immediately picked up the phone to speak to the Chief.

"What do you plan to do about those kids in front of Iva's?" the Mayor wanted to know.

"What would you do?" the Chief wanted to know.

"Get them the hell off the street," the Mayor said.

"Where the hell do you think this is, Russia?" the Chief said.

*

Before dinner and José Feliciano, Faith and I had a drink. Faith was drinking an Old-Fashioned. I had ordered a Miller Lite.

"What do you think of Iva's letter in the paper?" I asked.

"I think," Faith said, "the termites in Iva's hair have finally eaten through to her brain." Faith was referring to the bouffant hair-style popular in the fifties and still popular with the sixtyish Iva. The ragged adornment atop Iva's head in fact rarely looked washed, rather as if she had lacquered it with successive applications of Spray Net.

I was surprised by this response. Faith is a feminist. So am I. It really makes a guy nervous when he can't rely on a woman's response to questions touching the issue.

"What is Iva complaining about? Kids gathering at a street corner?"

I always hate it when a lawyer leads her spouse.

"Is there any difference at the post office when you pick up the morning mail? You have to wade through a bunch of old people and nurses' aides to get to your mailbox. Is there anything more disgusting than the smell of old man Fountain's cigar smoke mixed with the stench of pig poop on some farmer's boots?"

I had to admit, she did have a point.

"What Iva and the other concerned citizens of Yelton don't like are the ear-rings, the tight sexy jeans, and the long hair. You don't direct the police to enforce a dress code," Faith said. . . . Lawyers can twist just about anything.

The Motleys stood on the corner, more or less oblivious to the controversy that raged about them. As a group, Motleys don't have a great sense of reality. I know all about Motleys. I wrote my Ph.D. thesis on Motleys.

Motleys come in all shapes and sizes, but they share one thing in common: Motleys are scared shitless.

They are afraid to trust anyone or love anyone. Motleys are also afraid to fail, which is why they rarely try anything . . . like work or school. They are, to put it shortly, afraid of life.

Another thing Motleys share is an innate ability to find each other, no matter what the town or city, to huddle together, to mill, to bunt, to push, to swear and spit, and later to put or poke things into their bodies that make them less afraid, like smoke from cannabis resin, alcohol, amphetamines, coke, smack, and heroin.

Pray your kids don't turn out to be Motleys!

While these terrified human beings were a pain in the ass to Iva, they were to a significant segment of the population, the stuff of life. Chief Shelton and his four constables depended upon them for their jobs. So, too, judges and lawyers, social workers, jail guards, civil servants, insurance brokers, and, occasionally, undertakers. . . . Fear puts a lot of bread on the table.

*

Roger Camp was a Motley's Motley. He stood on the corner, in front of IVA'S STATIONERY. It was chilly, so he smoked a cigarette. Motleys aren't the only ones who do that.

Camp yearned to be noticed. He was fifteen years old, bright, witty, and attractive. He was also scared shitless. Camp flicked his cigarette in a high arc into the passing traffic. Several shoppers noticed . . . and scurried across the street.

Camp felt the warmth caused by the shoppers' attention. It made him feel terrific. He let out a high shriek and hit a chubby Motley named Collins on the arm. Collins felt the warm glow of the staring shoppers too and yelled out, "Fuck you, Camp!" He shoved Camp just hard enough to rivet the onlookers' attention. The old folks sped away. The two boys laughed excitedly.

*

Mitch Hepworth had practised law in Yelton for thirty-five years. He arrived fresh from law school and had rented a storefront directly opposite the town's two chartered banks.

The first thing Mitch Hepworth had done was to have his name painted in black letters on the front door:

MITCHELL HEPWORTH B.A., LL.B.,
BARRISTER, SOLICITOR
and NOTARY PUBLIC.

He then blocked the storefront window with dark green curtains. These same curtains kept prying eyes out of the office for twenty-five years. As times changed, Hepworth replaced the faded green fabric with silver sprayed onto his storefront window. Hepworth had the largest one-way mirror in the county.

Aside from this technological innovation, little else had changed in Hepworth's office in thirty-five years. The law books he had brought from law school still lined his walls. None had been added. Hepworth had little use for changes in the law. It meant confusion in his life, and uncertainty. Uncertainty frightened Hepworth. He hated it.

For greater certainty, Hepworth had not changed his secretary either. Other secretaries had come and gone, but Hattie Smale, who seemed old when Mitch Hepworth arrived, thirty-five years before, stayed on. Hepworth had not changed his dress code either. For thirty-five years he wore dark blue pin-striped suits . . . with matching vest. His closet at home was filled with them. To Hepworth the three-piece suit represented the law, better even than the blindfolded lady with the scales of justice. Hepworth asked of the law only one thing: the opportunity to make a decent living. This he did by handling the estates of departed friends who in life had entrusted their wills to him, and by acting in real estate transactions for their heirs.

He had learned to deal with the bothersome changes in the law by sending Hattie to lectures offered for secretaries by the Law Society. What changes Hepworth needed to know, he learned from Hattie.

Mayor Smith would have rather sent the town's little legal problem to Faith, but friendship still counted in Yelton. His friend Mitch Hepworth was also upset when he learned he was expected to draft a by-law prohibiting loitering and causing a disturbance in town. He too wished the matter had been referred to Faith. A by-law authorizing a debenture to finance sewer systems was one thing, but a quasi-criminal by-law ... how was Hattie expected to know that?

*

Faith and I ordered dinner before José Feliciano took to centre stage. Faith ordered Sole Bonne Femme ($26.50). I ordered the special, poached salmon ($21). I don't remember the name of the white wine, but it was one of the cheapest on the list ($18). This was a long way from Yelton, where quality is measured by size of serving. No *cuisine minceur* in Yelton ... good honest folk, good honest food!

The clients I worked with, through the Children's Aid, of course ate differently: too many chips, too many burgers, too much soft white bread. The diet left the women puffy and fat, the men grey and thin.

Out of Puffy by Grey came Motley kids ... those damn kids. Even if you did take them to the Royal York Hotel, they'd still order a burger and fries.

I love those kids. I really do. That's why I work for the Children's Aid. If it were up to me, I'd bring them all home and love them back to health. If you want to know the truth, my mother read Dickens's "A Christmas Carol" to me once too often ... I mean, I believe all that stuff that Charles Dickens wrote. I believevein old Fessiwig and poor Fan and Bob Cratchit and Tiny Tim. I believe in it all year round and it breaks my heart.

I told this to Faith, that night at the Royal York Hotel, before she gave José Feliciano a standing ovation. Faith, who has always acknowledged my "caring," took my hand and gave it a squeeze. She looked at me with loving eyes and murmured, "It's systemic."

"It's what?" I asked.

"Systemic," she repeated. "You're part of the problem."

*

Yelton's council meet the second Thursday of each month, on the second floor of the Town Hall. This seat of power in its former life had been a hotel. The council chamber had been a ballroom. Now dances are held on the Arena floor . . . dancing has become more of a sports event. The former ballroom also accommodates spectators, who rarely come, and the press, who rarely miss.

The local weekly paper is owned by Red Lampley. Lampley bought *The Yelton Weekly News* some years earlier and renamed it *The Yelton Beacon Harold*. Few noticed the error and fewer cared enough to comment. Lampley himself discovered the error over a bottle of beer at the hotel one night after a council meeting. Mayor Smith mentioned it. Lampley replied, "If anyone can tell me what in hell *Beacon Herald* means, I'll change the masthead; otherwise it remains the same." No one ever did.

Lampley had a policy of hiring the least experienced editorial staff he could lay his hands on. This afforded him two personal objectives: the first was to pay as little as possible, the second, to ensure that his unstated policy was respected.

Red's unspoken policy was: "NO NEWS IS GOOD NEWS!"

Red felt certain his readers got all the news their stomachs could bear from the six-o'clock TV news. He dreaded being the bearer of bad news. Red was afraid that one day someone might shoot the messenger. Red also feared being poor. He wasn't prepared to pay for a lot of reporters to cover the courts or other institutions. On occasion, if the local police provided a list, Red would publish the names of kids charged with breaking into the liquor store. He never did publish the names of those who went to trial and were acquitted.

Red didn't publish the names of citizens convicted of impaired driving either, or of beating their wives or sexually assaulting their kids or cheating on their income tax.

He didn't want to pay his reporters to dig up stories either . . . about incompetence and bad planning at the local hospital, or about farmers who dumped liquid manure into the local creeks that fed into the town's water source, or about the town sewer system that was also polluting Yelton's water during spring runoff.

Instead, Red developed a string of informants who reported monthly about the goings-on at their local service clubs, viz. Rebecca's, Optimist, IOOF, Lions, Lionesses, and UCW. Even the Brownies reported monthly to Red's *Beacon Harold*. The lowly paid editorial staff were kept busy editing these reports and reporting from the minutes of council. Fairs and festivals filled the pages too: fall fairs, town fairs, bean festivals, threshermen reunions, and Klompenfests. The *Harold* also featured "News From A Hundred Years Ago."

Readers could always count on at least one editorial, often scalped from some other Ontario weekly. And sometimes Red himself would sit down at the old

Underwood and pound out his own homily-filled, fighting editorial, such as this one:

> Readers of these pages will be aware of the by-law proposed by council ostensibly to keep our streets safe for seniors and others from kids with nothing to do. We can't help but feel that there has to be a better way.
>
> Fifteen cents of every dollar collected in this county is spent on social services. Frankly, sometimes we wonder where that money goes.
>
> Is this really a police matter? We don't think so. The police have got enough to do already without the added burden of baby-sitting a bunch of disrespectful and rowdy kids. The old adage, children should be seen and not heard, is still true. It's up to parents, and if they won't do it, social workers, to see that the old adage is obeyed.
>
> R.L.

*

None of the eight members of town council saw themselves as being part of the democratic process. In spite of this, or maybe because of it, they represented the townspeople well. Roads were well maintained and, except for the spring-runoff pollution problem, municipal services were provided without a hitch.

To its further credit, council accurately reflected the opinion of the vast majority of Yeltonites. Here is a copy of the clerk's notes following the meeting agenda, taken during a regular council meeting:

EDUCATION . . . Resolution to support bilingual education in the local public school — DEFEATED. (Would the town also have to provide Chinese instruction for the children of the couple who own The Sun Woo Chinese and Canadian Cuisine Restaurant on Main Street?)

CAPITAL PUNISHMENT . . . Resolution circulated to all municipal councils by the John Howard Society urging Parliament to retain abolition of the death penalty—DEFEATED. (Without discussion.)

ARTS AND RECREATION . . . (a) Request from local theatre group for financial assistance—DEFEATED. (User benefit/user pay through ticket sales, bake sales, etc.)

(b) Request from Arena Committee to purchase new Zamboni and ice-cleaning machine to replace present crippled unit—PASSED. (Repairs would be almost as much as new unit.)

(c) Resolution to authorize issue of liquor permit to Junior Farmers for banquet, casino night, and dance—PASSED. (Without discussion.)

PUBLIC SERVICES . . . Resolution to purchase used grader for snow clearing and general road maintenance—PASSED. (Without discussion.)

SOCIAL SERVICES . . . Resolution to provide financial assistance for county-wide "safe house" for battered women—DEFEATED. (Taxpayers' money already budgeted for social services. Additional grant would be double taxation.)

GENERAL GOVERNMENT . . . A by-law to reg-

> ulate noise, loitering, and general conduct on town streets—PASSED. (After general discussion supporting the by-law.)

And so on.

CHAPTER TWO

MAGIC QUESTION NUMBER TWO:
What in fact did you end up with?

By the fourth session Faith was so angry, she hardly talked to me between sessions. I told you, this was no picnic. Here is more or less what Faith told the marriage counsellor:

"For a guy who works with people, he sure is lousy in his relationships. My husband confuses caring with controlling. Life with a Messiah is a constant power struggle. To this day I don't know if I chose law school or he did.

"He decorated my office, our house, my body. On my weekend we spend it with his friends. He is so crazy, he likes the house cleaned from the bottom to the top. (The dust floats up!) He also likes the toothpaste squeezed from the bottom to the top. At least he is consistent.

"He likes to lie in the sun in February. (He says I need the sun so I don't get rickets.) I like to ski. He is mad about his clothes closet, his shoes, and his suits. I like to pitch my clothes on the chair at the end of the day. Who the hell ever sits on a chair in the bedroom anyway?"

Faith was really cookin' . . . who needs this shit?

"What did I expect?" Faith continued. "He is a social worker, after all. . . . If you want to be saved, follow a social worker. If you want to be loved and cared for, you're better off joining a cult.

"Do you know what the secret phrase among social workers is?" Faith continued. "It's PLAN-OF-CARE. That's it, PLAN-OF-CARE.

"The PLAN-OF-CARE is the social workers' final solution to your problem (and to his problem too). It's their plan for your miserable little life so that you can grow up just the way they think you should. It's like the Pritikin diet. You follow their plan and life will unfold as it should. Do they care? Do you doubt they care? Why else would they devise a plan if they didn't care? Shit!"

*

I didn't tell you, but one of the rules of this marriage counselling is that you're not allowed to interrupt your spouse when he or she is talking. Good rule, huh? . . . I wonder what I would have said anyway.

*

Faith wound it up this way: "Social workers get off on power. They mistake care for caring. They think their motive is love . . . caring for the needy. In fact, it's their fear, their insecurity . . . their need to be in control. I pity the people they care for, the people they control. Some days I pity me. I'm sick of control."

Faith also said we didn't communicate well and that I didn't trust her. . . . Want to know what I said?

I said I didn't really see anything too radically wrong at all. To tell you the truth, I was pretty content. I really cared about that girl.

*

But holy shit! Had I released a monster? Faith was hardly the sweet thing I had courted. As an undergraduate she was what you might have described as interesting but not interested.

I, on the other hand, was very much involved, issue-oriented. It was I who felt, and rightly so, that for her own good Faith should consider a career that took her out of the home. I feared, I really did, that Faith would collapse into housewife and mother, waiting for me, like some kind of pit bull, to share her day of dirty diapers and the like; of running off to some important meeting, like a day care board meeting or child abuse co-ordinating committee meeting.

If I was totally honest, I might have even been afraid that in her boredom Faith might have become involved with some other equally committed man . . . in her boredom.

You think I'm terrible? Christ, it happens every day.

Faith accused me of setting out on a campaign to "direct" her into the law. Well, why the hell not? What are friends for? I mean, when you consider the alternatives.

Anyhow, by the third year of her undergraduate studies, Faith herself decided to go into law. That was her decision, finally, not mine. On the whole, I think she decided rightly, up to a point. Suddenly, off went the blue angora, down went Milton and Keats, and out came sweat-shirts, jeans, and Linden on Torts. By then it was too late for me. I had stimulated an unexpressed agenda . . . and we were already married.

I was alone, as Faith hit the books. At least I was right on one point: Faith had no time for affairs and that was for sure.

Our well-run apartment, which I used to love coming home to, took on the appearance of a boot camp—

dishes in the sink, clothes on doorknobs and chairs, and notepaper and books everywhere.

As I said, I'm a feminist and proud of it. I have always helped out: the laundry, vacuuming, dishes . . . the lot. But I'll be goddammed if I'm going to do it all, alone.

You think I'm old-fashioned to pine for soft breasts covered by blue angora?

Want to know what I think about social work? I think it's a waste of time. How do you help someone who chooses burgers and fries over *table d'hôte*? It's too late. As long as you have issue out of Puffy by Grey, what can you do? What would you do? Don't complain to me!

Roger Camp's mother didn't complain. Why should she? She was, after all, the beneficiary of Mother's Allowance, subsidized housing, health care and dental plan, a fuel heat subsidy, and a drug plan. And when Roger was lighting fires at school, and later in it, who was appointed by the court to supervise mom and give her tips on rearing her eleven-year-old pyromaniac son? Me!

Where was Mr. Camp when we needed him? Where indeed!

And what was the magic figure on the imaginary line conjured up by statisticians to measure the waistlines of puffy Mrs. Camp and her three kids? In Yelton . . . poverty line: $14,500!

And what did Mrs. Camp receive free of charge for

herself and her three kids? . . . $9,800 . . . Missed by that much!

Don't complain to me!

*

It was 11:30 P.M. by the time Faith and I got out of the Royal York Hotel. Faith was still humming "Come On Baby, Light My Fire" as we headed out of the city to our world in Yelton.

"What exactly did you mean," I asked, without the slightest hint of aggression in my voice, "when you said that it's systemic?" The singing stopped.

There was a long pause. I looked over at Faith. Tears were streaming down her cheeks. Can you imagine it? One minute the woman is singing "Come On Baby, Light My Fire," and the next minute she is crying. . . . And you mean to tell me there isn't a difference between men and women?

"What did I say?" I asked softly, and without the slightest hint of provocation. I was met with silence. "Do you want to talk about it?" I asked, without the slightest hint of manipulation in my voice.

Faith blew her nose and wiped her eyes, slowly and deliberately. I drove, waiting. I won't try to tell you I wasn't just a little bit nervous. Finally, after what seemed about a half an hour but was only a few seconds, Faith took a deep breath. I tightened my grip on the steering wheel. "You know," she began, and of course I didn't. "I go to that office of mine every day, and I see women who have been threatened or punched in the face by men, kicked in the groin, or burned on the buttocks by lit cigarettes. I see women whose eyes are black, women who have been stabbed, cut, or slashed by men. I see women whose teeth have been chipped or knocked out, whose arms or wrists or fingers have been twisted, or broken, by men. And they ask me what they should do!"

"It must make you very sad," I said helpfully.

Faith ignored me. "What is it with men?" she asked. "Why do they think they have the right to hit?"

I didn't say anything. To tell you the truth I've wondered the same thing myself.

"Look at the six-o'clock news, with all those men dressed in uniforms and hats marching around with guns, or making speeches defending acid that rains down on us, or killing almost extinct species of wild animals for profit. Why is it always men who make the headlines?" No news is good news, I thought.

"Even in this damn country, controlled by men," Faith went on, "poor women and children don't have adequate housing, clothing, health care, education, or food.

"It's systemic," Faith said, pushing a button that powered her car seat from upright into a temporary *chaise-longue*. "Men have created a system that is destroying the world."

I felt a little bit trapped by this last statement as Faith's head disappeared from my field of vision and was replaced by her feet. It seemed damn unfair to lump us all together. . . . Not all men, I thought. "I'm trying to make a difference," I ventured.

"I know," Faith said, just before she drifted off to sleep. "And I love you."

*

Saturday evening found the regular group of seven or so Motleys congregating at the four corners, in front of IVA'S STATIONERY.

It was the evening that Iva watched in horror as the Motleys carried out their ritual, bunting and pushing, swearing and spitting, right in front of Iva's entrance. She called the police, again, to demand that something be done.

The other town kids had gone to the movies or were involved in a baseball tournament held at the Kinsmen Park. Motleys rarely go to the movies, especially since the introduction of VCRS.

Motleys prefer to sit around in the comfort of someone else's house, eating chips, smoking cigarettes, and delighting in an array of sophisticated fire-power, lethal hands, and bare buttocks and breasts. If Motleys did go to the movies, it was generally to tear up seats, sit with cigarettes in the nonsmoking area, and make life miserable for young girls and anyone else who sat in the first three rows of the theatre.

As for organized sports, Motleys as a rule didn't. Three other places Faith pointed out you're unlikely to find Motleys: sun-tan parlours, by the bar at Hedonist II, and at Creed's.

*

Roger Camp was with the other kids on the corner, bunting and shoving and yelling and spitting. Roger wore a pair of tight grey jeans. He also wore high-cut running shoes done up . . . halfway . . . and a black T-shirt that featured the bust of Mozart on it with the inscription below the head. The inscription said "ROCK ME AMADEUS." Classy, huh?

A dresser in Roger's bedroom at home contained the rest of Roger's possessions. It held some underwear, a spare pair of blue jeans, several pairs of socks, white, with holes in the toes, two more shirts. One shirt pictured Jim Morrison with the message "THE DOORS FOREVER." The second shirt buttoned up the front. It was khaki in colour and had epaulettes on the shoulders, not dissimilar to a policeman's dress shirt.

Other items found in the dresser were a socket wrench set, with three of the eight sockets missing: miscellaneous school assignments, not turned in; an empty, wrinkled leather wallet, of indeterminate age; several grains of marijuana left from an earlier stash; a clip-on blue tie; a Phillips screwdriver; a photo-booth snapshot of Arnold Camp, Roger's father; and the December issue of *High Society*, Special Christmas Issue.

On top of the dresser was an inexpensive gold-coloured triptych containing three-by-five-inch photos of Roger. The first two were black and white. One pictured a plump infant of about three months, lying on his back, in a terry jump suit. The jump suit featured metal snaps from ankle to neck. Chubby legs were lifted and bent at the knees. Tiny perfect fingers formed into two neat balls held high above the head. And on the face the camera caught what may have been the biggest smile, before or since, spread across Roger's face.

The middle panel displayed a boy of about five. He wore short pants, a striped short-sleeved jersey, and low-cut runners, and no socks. In his arms he held a small terrier of some mixed ancestry. The mutt was just putting a tremendous lick on Roger's smiling face when the shutter tripped.

The last picture was in colour. It was a class picture, taken in Grade Three. It showed a thinner boy wearing a light yellow sweat-shirt, arms folded across the chest, brow furrowed, fuzzy eyes. Maybe Roger was starting to get scared.

*

I recently prepared a psychological profile of a young woman, Fancy Moroff, seventeen years old. Her lawyer asked me to do it for use in court on the matter of sentence. This seventeen-year-old had pleaded guilty to her fourth charge of shoplifting.

There were two things that interested me about this girl; the first was that she was, even at seventeen, irresistibly attractive. She looked like a young and innocent Cheryl Tiegs, with a smile that gave you a funny feeling in the pit of your stomach. The second thing was that she had fuzzy eyes.

I interviewed both parents as well as Fancy. Here is some of my report:

> BACKGROUND:
>
> The Moroffs are an upper-middle-class family. There are five children: three boys and two girls. Father reports working hard during Fancy's early years in order to make a success of his jam business, which started as a pick-your-own strawberry operation and grew into the Moroff Jam Company. Mother was primary care-giver to family. She also worked in the business during its early years. She reports the family are all in good health. There have been no problems reported with the other siblings.
>
> INTERVIEW WITH FATHER:
>
> Father says Fancy has had everything she needed or wanted, including his love. Father reports that Fancy does not listen to either

him or her mother. Fancy stays out until two and three in the morning, without explanation. She generally has one of the three family cars. She does little with the family and resents having to help around the house or with the family business. Father sees the problem caused by wife, who is too indulgent with Fancy. He says that when he says No to Fancy, his daughter can always count on her mother to say Yes. He thinks his wife is afraid of her daughter. Father also blames Fancy's friends, who are for the most part Motleys.

INTERVIEW WITH MOTHER:

Mother says Fancy was the last of her five children. She had not been planned. Mother confirms that Fancy has had everything a young girl should have while growing up, including her love. Mother says that Fancy does not obey the rules of the home and refuses to help mother around the house, or in the family business with even routine chores. Mother sees the problem caused by husband, who is too indulgent with Fancy. She says that when she says No to Fancy, her daughter can always count on her father to say Yes. She thinks her husband is afraid of his daughter. Mother also blames Fancy's friends, who are for the most part Motleys.

INTERVIEW WITH SUBJECT FEMALE:

Fancy is an attractive young woman of seventeen years. She has attended Yelton and District High School. She reports that her early good marks have declined over the past three years. She has just completed Grade Twelve, in the general course. She requires one credit in typing to get her diploma. She says she wants to be a designer, but seems unclear as to what she wants to design.

During our interview this youngster was unable to express herself easily. She avoided eye contact and spoke in a quiet monotone.

Fancy reports that her parents are always hassling her and won't let her live her own life. She admits to using alcohol and marijuana, but only moderately. She did not elaborate on how much was moderate. Fancy says she has never been able to talk to her parents, especially her mother. She sees nothing wrong with her present life-style. She admits to staying out "quite late" and being sexually active.

Fancy says she has no real plan for her future and does not see the need for one just yet. She would like "to hang out" with her friends for now. She confirms that her friends for the most part come from a lower socio-economic group, and that some have been involved with the law.

When questioned about the theft, Fancy admitted to several beyond those leading to charges. She expresses no remorse but says she will not do it again. Fancy says she got a certain sense of satisfaction when she got away with the thefts.

SYNOPSIS:

Fancy is an attractive seventeen-year-old girl of above average intelligence. She is before the courts for shoplifting nail polish, value 79¢. She is a repeat offender who, if left unsupervised, is likely to repeat the offence, despite her comments to the contrary. The young offender comes from an unremarkable family. None of her siblings has been in trouble with the law.

Her parents have been well-meaning, but it is clear they have never encouraged their daughter in her positive attributes. It is equally clear that they have not consequenced her for negative behaviour. The result is a young woman who gets a feeling of satisfaction out of getting away with petty theft. She also feels comfortable in the company of her friends, who are equally unmotivated.

RECOMMENDATIONS:

This young offender would benefit from a term of probation, which includes compulsory attendance in a self-awareness program. The whole family could also benefit from counselling.

Respectfully submitted:

Fancy appeared in Young Offenders' Court. She stood before the judge on her guilty plea, with her auburn hair shoulder length, her perfect smile, Benetton top, Ports slacks, and white Italian flats. She was given a suspended sentence and put on probation for six months. One of the conditions of her probation was that she attend whatever counselling her probation officer directed.

I pity her probation officer.... There is no self-awareness program available that I know of, and family therapy will take six years, not six months. Don't blame me... I just write the reports and make the recommendations!

*

I had been assigned by the Family Court to work with Roger's mother, Diane, after he had set his first fire at the public school.

"What kind of help do you need?" I asked Diane Camp.

"Well," she said, "we could use some money. I think the kids are getting sick of macaroni and cheese."

"How about burgers and fries?" I said. "There's no more money available."

"How about getting someone in to look after the kids while I take a nurses'-aide course, so I can make enough money to dress the kids properly?"

"Where do you take a nurses'-aide course?" I asked.

"In Stratford."

"How will you get there without a car?" I asked.

"I don't know," she replied.

"Don't worry about it," I said. "We don't have a program that provides support for working mothers anyway."

"What are you offering then?" she asked.

"How about a Big Brother?" I suggested.

"You think that will help?" she asked.

"Not really," I said.

CHAPTER TWO

*

Diane Camp was thirty-seven. She looked forty-five. She had been attractive before she got puffy. Diane was still bright, and witty too. In my judgement she suffered from only one serious flaw: she was too submissive. Why not? She had been brought up to say Yes. She was afraid to say No.

This flaw had brought her some pleasure and some pain.

Sometimes she didn't know which she liked better. Diane said Yes to booze, Yes to men, and Yes to Roger, as in:

"Can I go out?"

"Yes."

"Can I stay out?"

"Yes."

The night Iva called the police on Roger and his friends, Diane was saying Yes to a joint made of marijuana, and to a friend named Norman.

I suppose Diane said Yes to Roger because she loved him. They had a ritual, those two, that they shared. Whoever got home first after a night out waited for the other to arrive so that they could share the early hours of the morning together.

Sometimes Diane would simply hold her son in her arms, in their dimly lit kitchen, whispering to Roger how much she loved him before sending him off to bed. Sometimes they would make popcorn or order in pizza or smoke a joint together, and laugh and laugh as each one, mother and son, told some safe part of that evening's events.

And as the sun came up they would hug and tell

each other how much they loved the other, mother to son and son to mother.

Diane had been out when Constable Bowles called the house, as required by law, to tell Roger's mom that Roger was being held at the police station.

If Diane had known about that evening's events, she would have said "NO!"

*

Faith always kids me about social workers' vocabulary. She says social workers fall in love with trite words and expressions, like no other profession, such as:

PLAN-OF-CARE
Notion
Inappropriate
Dad
Siblings
Consequencing

I do admit there is something in what Faith says, but you can't use the word "consequencing" too much to suit me. That's what I eventually settled on for Diane Camp's PLAN-OF-CARE: consequencing. She had to punish young Roger when he acted inappropriately; otherwise how was he, or any kid, going to learn?

Frankly, I think consequencing is the essential tool in the parenting tool-box. How else can children be expected to learn unless inappropriate behaviour is dealt with by appropriate punishment?

How indeed! I see it every day in my job. Parents refuse to say No for fear their kid might pout. To these parents the pout is mightier than the sword. Our agency has spent hundreds of thousands of dollars supervising parents, in teaching them to say No! . . . Usually it's too late.

I mean, what's a parent to do? You can have the best PLAN-OF-CARE in the world for your kid, but if you're afraid of him or her, if you don't include the odd corporal manifestation of parental love, you might as well forget it. . . . If you don't believe me, ask Roger's mother, or Mr. and Mrs. Moroff for that matter.

Of course there is always the risk, as the child grows older, that he or she will ignore the parent anyway. . . . I have always thought of my job as an art, not a science.

Chief Shelton had been disciplined by his father in ways that shaped his life profoundly. When he was very young, if young Shel misbehaved, his father simply ignored him, treated Shel as if he were transparent. Dead.

This strategy tended to catch young Shel's attention. He would go nuts trying not to misbehave and, when inevitably he did, Shel would go nuts trying to catch his father's attention. This often led to further transgressions and further isolation and so on.

As Shel got older, his father added to his consequencing arsenal by withholding things Shel wanted or needed.

Shel began to notice that sometimes punishment was arbitrary. Even when he committed no offence, favours could be withheld. He noticed, when he was seventeen, that family car privileges were apt to be withdrawn by his dad, almost on a whim, for some imagined or picayune transgression. He also noticed that the more important the event was to him, the more he relied on his dad, the more likely he was to be consequenced.

It could still bring on a pretty fair headache when he recalled the time he had worked up enough nerve to ask Rosalie Blum to the high school graduation dance. Who was Rosalie Blum? The most delicious high school co-ed ever to put on a blue angora sweater, that's who.

Shel had suggested they double-date to the dance with Rosalie's best girl-friend, Cherie (the cheerleader) Morris. Cherie dated Gregg Scott. Who was Greg Scott? Only the president of the high school student council, captain of the football team, honour student, and generally regarded as the coolest guy in school, that's who.

It had all come together so perfectly, the date, the double date with Cherie and Gregg, the gardenia corsage, the perfect haircut, for a change the clear complexion on a day that counted. Shel strolled into the kitchen where his parents sat talking. His pulse sped up. He could feel it in his ears.

"Hi, Dad," Shel said. "Can I have the keys to the car?"

"Did you pick up the laundry after school, like I said?" Shel's dad asked. You'd have to say Shel's dad was a consummate consequencer.

Shel not only grew up to obey the law; he even became the Chief of Police of Yelton, Ontario.

*

The Chief received Iva's call at 11:00 P.M. He was at home watching the local news. It's hard for the Chief of Police to go to the local hotel, or anywhere for that matter, in a small town.

Iva was loaded for bear. "I'm one of those that pay your salary," Iva reminded the Chief. This cut very little ice with the Chief. He believed himself woefully underpaid. He was probably right.

"Get out there and get those kids away from my doorway," Iva demanded. "You've got no more excuses. We've got a law in this town that says no one is allowed to loiter. Enforce it!"

"Ah, Iva, where the hell are the kids going to go? What harm are they doing anyway?"

"Let 'em hang around your front door or at the police station," Iva spat back. "Better still, let 'em hang around the inside of the station; that's where they belong."

"OK, Iva," the Chief said. "Leave it with me. I'll take care of it."

The Chief was scheduled to meet his force the next afternoon to review the occurrence sheet and work out the duty roster with his four constables. He dreaded these meetings. He could take the men one at a time, or even in twos, but all four filled him with unspeakable rage. The Chief didn't know why.

The constables, to be fair, were very stupid men. Life had taken them aside when they were young and whispered into their hollow ears that they had best follow simple careers in which they were told exactly what to do . . . often. Police work in a small community had, as it turned out, been perfect for them.

The next afternoon the Chief watched the men from his office at the front of the station as they shuffled into the tiny, windowless meeting room that also served as the interrogation room.

The ritual was always the same. Each of the men took his particular place around a small rectangular table that sat in the centre of the room. The room was lit by a lamp with a green metal shade that hung over the centre of the table. It was just like in the movies.

Each of the men pulled out a pack of cigarettes and disposable butane lighter and carefully put them in front of himself. Each smoked his own brand of cigarette. Ed Bowles smoked Export "A"s filter; Bruce Smyth smoked Player's Light; Walter Fitkin smoked Sportsman cigarettes; and Mel Roose preferred Vantage, green. Who said these men weren't individuals?

*

We live right in Yelton, in a large hundred-year-old yellow brick house. My parents think we're nuts to live in a big, drafty old house, just the two of us. So do most of the people of Yelton.

To Yeltonites, the degree of house perfection has nothing to do with high ceilings, wide casement windows, or original fireplaces. In Yelton, house perfection is directly proportional to the heat-retention factor (R factor).

To my knowledge only one home in North America has ever had a perfect R factor, and that was right in Yelton. Unfortunately, a family of four suffocated in that house one winter while quietly eating Sunday breakfast. The Fire Marshal did confirm, however, that the house was perfect. No cold air got in, and naturally, no warm air got out.

Sometimes even perfection is consequenced.

I love our old place. So does Faith. I love to come home and dust her and polish her. I love to wipe her old counters until they shine, and run the vacuum over her old wooden floors and our old Indian rugs. Conversely, I hate when anyone messes her up. Faith says

I'm compulsive . . . I think I'm neat. I've always been that way. So has my mother.

To tell you the truth, I'm not sure how I feel about the people of Yelton. They're quirky people, happy to see you on the street but not anxious to invite you into their well-insulated homes.

The people of Yelton greet you on the street with "Ge-day! How are you now?" or "Well, what de ye know te-day?" They seldom wait for the answer.

When you think of it, the greeting "What de ye know te-day?" is a rather formidable salutation. I mean, what the hell do you know today? Over the years I have worked on several answers, like "Not much!"

The answer always seems to satisfy my interrogators but has left me feeling somewhat inadequate. The best answer I ever heard was delivered by my wife Faith, the original answer-for-everything kid.

When asked by Al Thompson, a local feed-mill operator, "What de ye know te-day?" Faith replied, "More than yesterday and not as much as tomorrow!" She might just as well have said, "Not much."

Another thing I've noticed about Yelton is that people don't have a whole lot to say after the greetings. At Laurie's Light Lunch, for example, I've wandered in for coffee with the guys, especially on Saturday morning when Faith is working at her office.

It always starts out OK. The men are seated around the table, cigarettes sitting in little foil ashtrays, cupsa java steaming in front of them. As I walk in, all eyes lift. Faces light up in recognition, then: "Hey! What de ye know te-day?" I walk over, full of smiles, relieved to be with company, and I say, with as much sincerity as I can muster, "Not much." There is a general grunting and nodding of heads as I sit down . . . and then silence, more or less.

It drives me nuts. I mean, it's like the bend in the river: you never know what's ahead or behind. Were they in heated discussion before I came in? Do they gab when I leave? Is it possible they just . . . sit there? How the hell do I know!

I like good conversation. I really do. Maybe that's why I'm addicted to talk radio. I'm ashamed to admit it, but every button on my car radio is set to a radio talk show or all-news station. I even get WBZ, Boston. I listen to CBC too, Radio Noon, and, of course, Cross-Country Check-Up on Sunday evening. I even have radios in most rooms of the house. For crying out loud, I wear my Walkman when I'm vacuuming!

*

CROSS-COUNTRY CHECK-UP; WHERE ARE YOU CALLING FROM, PLEASE?

"Scarborough."

"Go ahead, you're on the air."

"Am I on the air?"

"You're on the air."

"OK. I'm sick and tired of women complaining about their fate, about their roles, about who they are. They don't know how lucky they are, at home. They have been, from the dawn of time, in control of the world and they want to give it all up."

"How have they been in control of the world, sir?"

"Simple. The hand that rocks the cradle controls the world. Instead, today they whine about an equal opportunity to work on heavy equipment. How do you bring up kids from the cab of a diesel bulldozer? There's no

room in the cab for a cradle, and it's too noisy up there anyhow."

"Some women would say they want to be as free as men to choose their occupation, to be free from the monotony of housework."

"If my wife were still alive today, she'd tell them that raising kids is no duller than sorting mail or key-punch operating. And raising kids is more fulfilling than moving earth. Women still give birth, women still give nurture. Men move dirt. Does your guest ever wonder why the street corners are filled with kids smoking dope and cutting classes? Because their mothers are out moving dirt, that's why."

I wasn't the only one working with Roger who liked him. His teacher, Miss Drew, found him bright and funny too, on the few days he attended her Grade Eight classes.

For sure, Roger had certain educational shortcomings; for example, he couldn't multiply or divide too well, and his spelling was atrocious. He had made it to Grade Eight, not on his academic record, not on his attendance, but on the third and final criteria for promotion: feet and inches. If Roger had been in Grade Six, where he belonged, he would have been too big and too tall for the rest of his classmates.

As it was, he was older than most of the other kids in his class, and several inches taller. Roger sat at the back of the class. No one had to look around him.

Miss Drew had a bit of a crush on Roger, in a very innocent way. When Roger smiled, which was often in school, it seemed to light up Miss Drew's entire class. And when Roger was around, no one in the class dared give Miss Drew a hard time. Roger wouldn't stand for that.

Roger hated when people picked on others. He knew what it was like to be an underdog. If you were a nice person and a teacher of thirty-five or so kids, you could easily be classed as an underdog.

Roger was very good in English. He wrote very nice short stories for Miss Drew. They were often hard to read because of his spelling, but Miss Drew took the time to work them through. Here is one of Roger's stories that Miss Drew took home and worked over so that she could enter it in the school essay contest:

> Jim Gibbons didn't have a father. Never. All there was of Jim's father was a silver candlestick holder that Jim's father had given his mom, before he vanished. The silver candlestick holder stood on a shelf on a wall outside of Jim's bedroom.
>
> His mom had raised Jim by herself, and Jim thought she had done a pretty fine job of it. He sort of felt sorry for his mom having to bring a kid like Jim up all by herself. Jim wasn't easy and he knew it.
>
> Jim liked to raid the fridge, and it seemed his mom was forever working to keep it stocked for Jim. Jim also liked to screw around the school yard with his friends. He was always getting his clothes dirty or torn. It seemed to Jim that his mom was forever washing his clothes or buying him new stuff.
>
> Jim was already fourteen, but he hadn't done a thing for his mom. He felt badly about

that. She was doing so much for him. Then one night Jim got his chance.

Jim and his mom where at home alone. It was about eleven o'clock at night and Jim was in his bed, sort of dreaming. His mom was in the next room watching TV. In his dream Jim heard a knock on his mom's and his apartment door. He saw his mom get up to answer it.

In his half-dream Jim watched his mom open the door. Standing outside the door was a huge man with a beard and a T-shirt that barely covered his big stomach. The man looked like a motorcycle outlaw. The outlaw pushed Jim's mom into the room and slammed the door shut behind him.

Maybe it was the slamming door that woke Jim up. Maybe it was his mom's cry. Jim sat bolt upright in his bed. Jim heard a thump. He heard his mom's cry again.

Jim raced to his bedroom door and flung it open. There in the middle of the room, on the floor, lay his mom. The motorcycle outlaw was sitting on top of her.

For a moment Jim was confused. Is this still a dream? he wondered. There was no time for thought. The huge man brought his arm up into the air to strike his mom again. Jim grabbed the candlestick holder that his dad had left for him and his mom and flew across the room at the motorcycle outlaw.

The outlaw looked up in surprise, but he was too late. The candlestick holder crashed against the side of his skull, sending blood in every direction. The motorcycle outlaw sank to the floor and lay still.

Jim had saved his mom.

The next morning Jim woke up and got out of bed. He quietly tiptoed into the living room. He wanted to see if he had dreamed the whole thing or if it had really happened. The candlestick holder sat on its regular place, on the shelf beside the door. He picked it up. It was bent. Was that the bend he put in it when he had used it as a hammer to hang a poster in his bedroom? It looked more bent than that this morning.

Jim walked over to the spot where the motorcycle outlaw had lain. There it was. On the carpet. Blood. Or was it the grape juice he had spilled when he was seven?

*

Roger did not win the essay contest. He was a no-show on the day the contest was held.

Miss Drew was pretty brave herself, out there alone. Teaching a bunch of kids exploding into puberty.

Miss Drew was twenty-eight. She was blond. She thought of herself as being pert. She was bang-on. Miss Drew lived alone in a two-bedroom apartment. It was decorated in frosty whites and pinks. Miss Drew had a pert apartment.

Miss Drew drove a 1987 Fiero. Sky-blue. Miss Drew had many dates over the years, but she had not yet found Mr. Right. Men liked to look at Miss Drew; liked her pert figure, her blond hair, cut short; liked to watch her get into and out of her sky-blue Fiero.

Miss Drew had liked many of her escorts too. She

liked going out with them to restaurants, liked having a glass of white wine with them, liked to go dancing with them. But Miss Drew had one thing she did not like. One thing Miss Drew did not like at all. Miss Drew did not like tongues, and the men she liked were constantly trying to put their tongues into her mouth . . . ECH!

She tried to explain this to a few of the men she really liked. She told them how much she liked being with them, dancing with them, eating and drinking with them. "But," she said, "I don't like when you try to stick your tongue in my mouth . . . ECH!"

Word gradually got out of Miss Drew's distaste for things lingual and she went dining and dancing much less. That was OK with Miss Drew too. She had her kids at school. All she had to put up with from them was some occasional lip. And when Roger was in class, she didn't even have to put up with that.

Her kids liked her too, especially the girls. The girls liked her looks. Those hormone-driven thirteen- and fourteen-year-old girls loved Miss Drew's pert style. The girls could feel their own heat increasing almost daily. It was with them wherever they went and whatever they did. They could feel it in the V of their acid-washed Levis. They could feel it blow between their legs in their thigh-high minis. They could feel it in their very souls.

Cool Miss Drew. Frosty Miss Drew. They envied her the cool peace she appeared to enjoy as she got into and out of her 1987 Fiero. They talked to Miss Drew about girls' basketball, about careers, about children and how they didn't want to have any until they were thirty-four, about drugs and alcohol, about relationships. They even talked to her about birth control.

They would have liked to reach out and touch the pert Miss Drew. Somehow, they never did.

*

Intimacy was another area that Faith and I struggled with during our marriage. Who doesn't? I mean, who teaches you how to be intimate, can you tell me that?

Who was your role model, smarty pants? Tell me it was your parent. OK? And don't laugh.

Maybe it was your Grade Eight teacher or *The Young and the Restless*. How about Blondie and Dagwood? Maggie and Jiggs? Mickey and Minnie Mouse? Pinocchio and Geppetto? Romeo and Juliet? Masters and Johnson? Linda Lovelace and Harry Reems?

Well, I'm waiting. Who DID teach you how to be intimate? Maybe you don't think intimacy is important. If you don't, you're wrong. Believe me. I have my Ph.D. in social work . . . for all the good it does me.

*

Roger heard intimacy, as much as he saw it, from Diane's bedroom, which was separated from his own by two very thin pieces of Gyproc. Diane was very intimate with a number of suitors who came to call. Diane was a complete and utter sucker for a tongue in her mouth. The first few times Roger heard intimacy, it scared the shit out of him.

*

As Roger's case worker, I became concerned about Roger's increasing independence from parental control when he was nine, as well as his propensity for lifting items of worth that weren't tacked down to a table.

Diane herself expressed concern.

"Diane," I said, "this business about Roger staying out all night has got to stop."

"I know," she replied.

"You've got to exercise some form of discipline over the boy," I said.

"I know," she replied.

One thing about Diane: she wasn't hard to get along with.

"You've got to tell him NO! Diane," I said.

"I do," said Diane.

"And what happens?" I asked.

"He just agrees with me and then does whatever he pleases."

"Have you tried grounding him or even giving him a good crack?"

"Does the dwarf wrestler Little Mister T challenge Andre The Giant?"

"Are you saying you can't handle him?" I asked.

"That's what I'm saying," Diane Camp said.

*

The thing I like best about my job is that we have an answer for everything. I mean, if your kid is out of control, call us. . . . We're in the book.

The answer I had for Roger Camp involved hauling him before the court, as a child in need of protection, and asking the judge to put him in either a group home or a foster home. Either way, Roger was saying bye-bye to his own little bedroom.

The last time I brought Roger before the court as a kid out of control, and therefore in need of protection, I asked the court to allow me to place him in a foster home.

*

I have often wondered what a courtroom looks like to a kid. Over the years I have asked several of them what the courtroom looked like to them. The answers have always been the same.

Here is what they said: "I dunno."

"Does it seem very large?" I would prompt.

"Yeah," they answered.

"What about the judge?" I would ask. "Sitting way up on that raised dais in his robes?"

"I dunno."

"Do you get scared?"

"Yeah," they answered.

"Do you get anything out of court?" I asked.

"Yeah," they answered.

"What?" I asked.

"I dunno," they answered.

*

The judge who heard Roger's case on that date was Judge Donald Brigham. Judge Brigham was sixty years old. He had recently been appointed to the bench as a Family Court judge. He had applied for the position because after thirty years of closing real estate deals and appearing on behalf of impaired drivers and petty criminals, he was tired of private practice.

He was a nice man. What he didn't know about children, he knew about the law.

I stood in the witness-box giving my evidence touching the facts on Roger's case. I never really worried about giving evidence in court. I figured what I didn't know about the law, I knew about children.

"The mother's in court today, Your Honour," I said.

"Where's the father?" the judge asked.

"Where indeed?" I answered.

The judge looked into the body of the court. He saw half a dozen of my colleagues sitting on the hard benches, waiting for their cases to be called. He also saw Diane and Roger, sitting up at the counsel desk. Their eyes were glazed over. God knows where their minds were.

"The application before Your Honour today is to place Roger Camp in a foster home. His mother is unable to control this twelve-year-old boy."

"Is that true, Roger?" the judge asked the twelve-year-old boy who looked to be sixteen.

"Yeah," said Roger.

"Stand up," the seated judge said to the still-seated Roger.

Roger shuffled to his feet. He now looked about fourteen.

"Is that true?" repeated the judge.

"I dunno," Roger answered.

"Is this true, Mrs. Camp? You can't control this boy?"

Diane got to her feet slowly. She could feel tears filling her eyes. "He isn't a bad boy, really," said Diane. "He just doesn't listen to me. I think maybe he needs a man in the house, which we don't have."

Judge Brigham looked the puffy, red-eyed Diane Camp over. He decided he wouldn't apply for the job. "Is that true, Roger? You don't listen to your mother?"

"Yeah," said Roger. He could feel the tears forcing their way through his throat and up into his eyes.

"Is this a way a boy treats his mother?" the judge asked.

Roger remained silent. He swallowed the tears back onto his burning palate.

"Well, is it?" the judge persisted gently.

Tears rolled down Roger's cheeks. Roger looked twelve years old again. The judge had made him look his age.

"No," said Roger.

Judge Brigham turned to me and asked, "What exactly does this boy do?"

"Well, Your Honour," I said, "Roger stays out all night, he has missed thirty-seven of the last forty-eight schooldays. He has been picked up by the police for drinking behind the dry-cleaning plant in town. The only time he spends at home is to sleep, to change his clothes and shower. He refuses to listen to his mother, the school, or to me for that matter."

"Is that true, Roger?" the judge asked the twelve-year-old.

Roger affirmed by nodding his head.

"I can't hear you," the judge persisted gently.

"Yeah," Roger croaked through his aching throat.

"This is a very drastic step to take, Mrs. Camp," the judge said to Diane, "taking the boy out of his house and placing him in a foster home. Is there anything else that can be done for the boy?"

"Like what?" Diane asked.

The judge frowned. Judge Brigham looked over at me.

"Your Honour," I said, looking over my notes, "Roger has been before this court on four different occasions already. We have tried probation and counselling. We put in a special PLAN-OF-CARE, which Roger ignored, or his mother was unable to carry out. We think he needs a more structured environment."

"Well, Roger," Judge Brigham began, "apparently

your mother can't control you, and we can't have that. Do you understand?"

Roger affirmed with his head. There was a moment's silence. "Yes," said Roger.

"This court has given you every opportunity to get your act together and to listen to your mother, and you have chosen to ignore it. Is that right?"

"Yes," said Roger. Roger looked at his feet. His eyes were dry again. He looked fourteen on his way to sixteen again. Roger's mind was God knows where.

"We just can't sit by and watch you run wild in the streets. You have to go to school like everyone else. You have to go to bed and get up in the morning like everybody else. In short, Roger, you have to start acting like everybody else. Do you understand?" Judge Brigham asked.

"Yeah," said Roger.

"I'm going to make a finding that you are a child in need of protection, and leave it up to the Children's Aid Society to find a proper placement for you. I hope that the next time I see you it will be to terminate this Order and return you to your mother and your home. Do you understand this?" the nice judge asked towards the body of the court.

"Yes," said Roger to his feet.

*

Luke and Frieda Van Erp were foster parents. Nice people, the Van Erps. Luke worked at the egg-grading station. He was a cleaner. Luke had swept a lot of shells in his day. Luke was fifty-four, small, and skinny. Luke rarely spoke unless spoken to.

What is it they used to say? Opposites attract? Frieda

was forty-five, a tall, powerfully built woman with a large bust. Frieda liked to talk. She also wanted to become a foster mom.

I interviewed Frieda Van Erp shortly after she applied to become a foster parent. We sat in the spotless kitchen of her spotless insul-brick two-storey home. Luke was there too, sitting at the Formica-and-aluminum kitchen table sipping tea from a mug. Luke wore a yellow-and-blue baseball cap. The cap had something to say. It said "GET CRACKIN'."

Frieda sat at the head of the table wearing a large blue cardigan that covered her large shoulders and expanded chest. She held her mug of tea in one hand and a smouldering cigarette in the other.

"So, Frieda and Luke," I said, "you want to become foster parents."

Frieda took a drag on her cigarette, mashed the butt into an aluminum ashtray that sat before her, and wiped away some invisible ash from the table surface.

"Yeah," she said. "Mrs. Groothuis at our church took me to a foster parent meeting last spring. She's a foster parent. I'll tell you the truth: if Mildred Groothuis can be a foster parent, I figure I can do it too. There's a woman that can't even keep cats, let alone take care of kids."

"Oh?" I asked.

"Sure," said Frieda. "I don't think she knows you gotta keep the Kitty Litter box changed."

"You don't have to know too much about cats to take care of kids," I said.

"Mildred Groothuis has two daughters," said Frieda, rolling her eyes. "Both of them got pregnant before they were out of high school. It wouldn't have hurt to know something about alley cats," Frieda said.

"Hmmm," I said. Our agency had considered Mildred Groothuis one of our best foster parents.

"All three of our boys finished high school and have jobs of their own." Frieda said triumphantly. "I brought those boys up right. They all learned early on that Yes meant Yes and No meant No."

"Some of our kids have problems," I said. "Some have never been taught Yes and No. Some have broken the law. Some have been abused by their parents. Some of them are pretty mixed up . . . you know what I mean?"

"Do you know Brenda Mann?" Frieda asked. "She was at the foster parent meeting too. Brenda Mann is a little mouse of a woman. Can't keep her husband away from the hotel or the girls. It's a wonder you let any kid stay at their place."

"Hmmm," I said.

"She does it for the money," Frieda said.

Luke stirred. "How much do you people pay to keep kids anyhow?" he asked.

"Good question," I said. . . . It was a good question too. If we put kids into institutions with trained personnel, it costs our agency about $55 a day.

"We pay $12 a day, plus a clothing allowance. And of course if the kids need anything special, like glasses or medication, we pay that too," I said.

"Nobody getting rich keeping kids," Luke muttered. He was right there.

A week after our interview I drove Roger out to the Van Erp place. Roger later told me that Mrs. Van Erp was a great cook and that he had to keep his room very, very clean.

Four days later the twelve-year-old Roger hitchhiked the fifteen miles back to Yelton. He explained that he preferred his own bedroom. Roger promised he would listen to his mom, that he would go to school, that he would quit drinking behind the dry-cleaning plant. And he did too . . . for at least three weeks.

CHAPTER THREE

TELL ME THE TRUTH: DOES ANYONE KNOW A COUPLE who really enjoyed their honeymoon? I don't mean with pictures-by-the-pool-enjoy. I mean enjoy-enjoy.

I mean a honeymoon where a man and a woman are alone and I don't mean leave-us-alone-alone. I mean alone-alone. Kissing-and-clinging-alone. I mean, I-know-who-you-are-and-you-know-who-I-am-alone. I mean gentle-intimate-trusting-alone. You know what I mean?

I'm not sure that my marriage to Faith ever totally recovered from our honeymoon.

Hey. Do me a favour. Don't get smug, OK? We went to Nassau together, Faith and I. I've got the pictures on the cabana, by the pool, and in the ocean to prove it.

It didn't live up to the billing; I will say that. Do you remember the one about the girl who said to her magician groom after being locked in their honeymoon suite for three solid days: "If I see that thing do one more trick, I'm going to scream"?

Who the hell tells you what is humour and what is expected? I'll tell you the truth: I thought my role . . . my duty to Faith was To Serve And To Protect. I was so anxious the entire time that I didn't do very well at either.

For example, Faith gave me shit for tipping our black waiter more than the white one. I just wanted him to know that, as far as I was concerned, there was no difference between black and white.

Faith wanted to see around the island, and I got upset because I didn't know the first damn thing about the island. How could I? I had never been there before. I refused to join a tour arranged for hotel guests. Wouldn't you? I mean, whose obligation was it To Serve And To Protect my bride – Nicky Hilton's or mine?

I arranged to rent a car. I also studied a centre-fold diagram of Nassau that came in a guide-book left in our hotel room. My tour was wonderful until we got hopelessly lost in a black residential slum of galvanized-metal-clad hovels and barefoot kids running through broken glass and shards of metal. I kept looking for that waiter I overtipped. Where was he when I needed him? Where indeed. Finally I was forced to call the hotel and give them our location. They sent some smug white guy to lead us back.

That magician had the right idea. Keep her in the damn hotel room.

Did you know they have gambling in Nassau? I didn't. I had read *The Gambler* by Fyodor Dostoevsky. I had even studied the psyche of the compulsive gambler. A lot of good that did me when we entered the casino.

I'll be honest with you: I was terrified. I didn't know the difference between baccarat and chemin de fer. Do you? To this day I don't understand roulette, or craps for that matter.

And there I was, just like in the movies. Big as life. With my fresh, innocent bride. To Serve And To Protect.

"Oh, will you look at this," I said as we entered the casino, full of contempt. "All these insecure psychotics, hoping to prove that they count." Faith's eyes opened wide.

"Wow!" said Faith, surveying the glitter and feeling the excitement and sensuality of the room. "Let's have a little fun."

My head literally spun. I was suffering from acute insecurity vertigo, but I kept it to myself. I too surveyed the room looking for something familiar. Anything. Bond, I thought. Bond . . . Bond . . . Bond . . . James Bond. At last I caught sight of it. Something familiar . . . "Want to play the slots?" I asked.

"Come on," Faith said, grabbing my arm and leading me to the wicket to buy chips. "Let's play blackjack."

What did she expect of me, Faith? Was I there To Serve And To Protect? I doubt it . . . now. And what did she expect of herself? I'm sure I don't know . . . even now.

I do know when we went back to our honeymoon suite after our night at the tables, delirious from the excitement of the game, that I loved that girl. I loved her in a way I had never loved before. I loved her with every fibre of my soul, loved her tension, her excitement. I loved the way she kept counting the wad of bills she won. The flush in her cheeks. The tension in her exquisite body. At last, that night, I was the magician.

Officers Smyth, Bowles, and Fitkin had been given their orders: Make the streets safe. Clear the pavement. Secure the four corners.

Fitkin drove the police cruiser along side streets to avoid notice from the bunting, shoving, swearing, spitting group of loiterers. All three men sat scrunched in the front seat. Nobody wanted to sit in the rear, behind the cage mesh. A block from the four corners, Smyth (whom the kids affectionately referred to as Rambo) was let out of the car. He started towards the four corners. He placed his right hand on the handle of his night-stick, which hung from his belt, for company. His pulse rate increased as he neared his target.

The police car, which was to provide back-up, turned off its headlights so as to make itself invisible and sped off into the night. The men had radio contact with each other, and Fitkin and Bowles could hear Smyth's increased breathing as he neared the four corners.

The Motleys all saw Smyth at the same time. They stopped their bunting, shoving, swearing, and spitting. A partially finished can of Labatt's Blue disappeared into a large planter. The planter had painted on its side a sign that said DONATED BY THE YELTON AGRICULTURAL SOCIETY. All the energy of the small band of boys and girls was directed towards the advancing constable.

One voice from the group called out an over-solicitous greeting to Smyth. Other voices mixed in the greeting. Smyth continued to come in silence, slowly and deliberately. The usually relaxed mob felt his tension and fell silent.

Roger had always been a leader, and called out to Smyth, "What de ye know te-day?" The rest of the group wondered out loud as well. Smyth was in no mood for enquiries. He continued to hold hands with his night-stick as he walked up to the throng. The two back-up partners pulled their unlit unit to the curb, just out of sight, a block away. They heard their partner request the crowd to disperse, peacefully, as well as the hostile response. This is exactly what was said:

"All right, you punks, move on."

"We ain't doin' nothin'."

"Get your asses the hell out of here."

"What for?"

"All right, Camp, I asked you guys nice, twice. Now I'm telling you to disperse. . . . Camp, you're under arrest for causing a disturbance, obstructing justice, and loitering."

As if by magic, the invisible squad car appeared at the curb-side. The rear door was opened and Camp's head was bent over for him so that he could clear the roof. Before you could say Nellie McClung, the car, the three officers, and Camp disappeared into the night.

*

When they arrived back at the station, Constable Bowles tried to contact Roger's mother as required by law after arresting a young offender. If she had been in that night, things might have turned out differently. As it turned out, Diane Camp, who was too submissive, was saying Yes to a joint made of marijuana, and to a friend named Norman.

*

The town was filled with rumours concerning Roger's death. The usually orderly group of seniors who picked up their mail at the post office lingered to talk about Roger, and about his death. The crowd grew large, pushing and bunting, chanting and swaying, so that you could hardly get to your box.

Grant Simpson, a successful retired banker, recalled

how he had helped the family out. He hadn't, of course, but you couldn't blame him for faulty memory. Simpson was seventy-nine, and he didn't always remember what had been done or said.

He had once explained to his son Stuart, after Stuart's graduation from Divinity College, what had made him a successful banker.

"Stuart," his father had said, "I always looked at people as fitting into one of two groups—those who needed my help and those who wanted my help. If someone really needed my help, of course they didn't get it because my help would have been no good to them. On the other hand, if they only just wanted my help, but didn't really need it, then they were truly ready to receive."

Stuart was puzzled by this piece of information. In the past, fatherly advice had been tolerated and ignored, whether understood or not. But this was special. It was, after all, graduation day. Perhaps his father was trying to pass on a message that might really matter to Stuart.

"I'm not quite sure I follow you, Dad," Stuart had said.

"Listen, Son," Stuart's father had said, placing his hand on Stuart's shoulder in a moment of unaccustomed intimacy, which made Stuart glad he had persisted in his question. "You can't help a builder buy tools if he hasn't got a job because he can't pay you back. If he gets a job, you can't help him to buy materials because he doesn't have the tools. And if he hasn't got tools, it's no use helping him buy materials. And without either materials or tools he'll lose the job, so there's no point in helping him buy either or both. . . . Do you see what I mean?

"On the other hand, if a person has his own resources, like materials and tools, you can help. There is something to build on. There is strength, there is a capacity to benefit from assistance. It's hard to help someone who is suffocating. They have to have some of their own oxygen.

"Damn it, Son," Grant Simpson went on, "it's the same in your business. In order to receive Christ, you have to be able to receive love. You show me a person who is struggling to breathe . . . suffocating, and who still has enough strength at the end of the day to love, and I'll show you the one in ten thousand I'd lend money to, even though they needed it."

"Ay-men," said Stuart.

"Remember that," said his father.

"I will," said Stuart.

*

My line of work doesn't lend itself to memory either. I had, as the CAS worker assigned to the Camp case, worked with Roger and his family almost from Roger's birth. I remember little success.

Roger had, as early as Grade Four, decided that nothing succeeds like absence. Roger stopped going to school. He was afraid that something ventured was something to be lost. And his mom was afraid of his mighty pout. Besides, Roger was already staying out most of the night.

Can I give anyone still in school a little tip? If you want to attract the attention of the system, but quick, stay away from school.

You can get into numerous fights, swipe small stuff from the neighbourhood convenience store, even feel girls up, on the way home from school, and for the most part you'll be OK, but skip classes and the full wrath of the system will descend upon you. I mean to say, there is even a special Provincial Act that deals with truancy. Be in school. Don't be wandering around and don't be at home sleeping. . . . They want to know where you are and what you're doing.

They don't even much care what you do in school. They guarantee a pass from year to year if you'll only just show up at class. Hell, everyone knows the primary purpose of school is state day care. Remember, if you pass attendance, you'll be promoted.

*

CROSS-COUNTRY CHECK-UP; WHERE ARE YOU CALLING FROM, PLEASE?

"I'm calling from Nanaimo."

"Could you turn your radio down, please?"

"OK?"

"What did you want to say to our guest?"

"That universal day care will be a complete disaster to our society."

"Why do you say that?"

"Why?"

"Yes."

"Because you can't have baby farms where infants are left at centres, to be watered, turned, fed, and changed by paid strangers. We're raising children here, not beef cattle. Children should be at home with a parent until they are at least three."

"Why should a woman have to stay home and give up a career until the child is three?"

"Why?"

"Yes."

"Because we're humans, not fish. Young children need their parents. Women don't give birth to toys that parents

are allowed to play with when they find the time. Women give birth to human life. And incidentally, who said anything about women staying home? If the father wants to stay home, let 'im."

"Regardless of who stays home, there are going to be economic losses in the marketplace."

"When I grew up, the marketplace existed to provide families with the things they needed to tend their children. Today the marketplace is the child. It is watched over, fussed with, talked about, cuddled, and worshipped, the way my parents did with us when we were young. My heavens, you can't even turn on a radio today without hearing whether the stock market's temperature is up or down. My parents didn't fuss with us near so much."

"I can tell the caller that studies have shown trained experts can do as well, and there is some evidence to support the notion that day care workers can do better than parents because they don't resent being with someone else's child all day long. This is so, as long as the parents are prepared to spend quality time with their child, before bed and on weekends."

"That's exactly the argument my kids used on me when they stuck me in this modern, state-of-the-art, god-forsaken senior citizens' home, here in Nanaimo."

*

Typically, Faith says the school system stinks. She says the system aims its punch at mediocrity. I agree with Faith. But who really wants their kid coming home full of crap the parent doesn't understand? Life is confusing enough without having kids who know more than we do.

> *"Hey, Dad, what do you think the effects of the theory of relativity were on religion in the twentieth century?"*
> "Fuck off, kid!"

And for those kids not quite able to reach mediocrity, the educators have invented ... LIFE SKILLS. This course cuts to the very core of society and teaches disadvantaged children exactly what they need to know.

> *"Hey, Dad, look at my report card. I aced Making Change and got a* B *in Ironing and Advanced Making Change."*
> "I'm proud of you, Son! Those life skills will get you through life . . . no problem!"

Think of it. We are educating a nation of paper-route delivery persons.

But will we be able to read the damn things when they are delivered to our door?

Who cares? At least the change will be right!

*

The *Yelton Beacon Harold* gave the story of Roger's death front-page treatment. There was a picture of Roger in the paper. It was a class picture taken the previous year, when Roger was fourteen. Roger had managed to miss 80 per cent of schooldays, but never missed a class picture day. It was as if he wanted to leave a record of his being in school pictures.

The article was written personally by the publisher, Red Lampley. This is exactly what it said:

> Roger Camp, 15, of Yelton, was found dead by his mother, Diane, this past Thursday. Roger, a Grade

Eight student, attended Yelton and District Community Public School.

Mrs. Camp stated that she had been brought home by a friend, only to discover her son, lying on the chesterfield, with blood coming from his mouth. She said it was her habit to meet with Roger at night and chat with him before retiring to bed. She stated that he had been watching World Federation Wrestling on the VCR when she discovered his body. The bout had been between Hulk Hogan and The Sheik.

The ambulance service and volunteer fire department were both summoned; however, the young Camp appeared dead on their arrival, and was officially pronounced dead at the Yelton and District Community Hospital by Dr. Ken Fellows. Mayor Smith was hunting at the time of the death and was therefore unavailable for comment.

Yelton Police Chief Shel Shelton expressed his regrets at the untimely death of the youth. He said that the police had earlier that evening questioned the boy at the station in regards to a loitering charge. The occurrence had taken place in front of IVA'S STATIONERY, Main Street. Chief Shelton explained that after a brief questioning the youth had been released on his written promise to attend court on the 14th of November on the charge. "At the time of his release," Chief Shelton said, "Camp was as healthy as you or I."

Roger is survived by his mother, Diane, and two younger brothers.

*

Kelson Weiler was sad to hear of Roger's untimely death. He was also glad to hear of Roger's untimely death. Kelson Weiler was a funeral director.

Weiler had lived his life in Yelton. As a high school student at Yelton and District High School, Kelson had landed himself a part-time job at Roller's Furniture.

That was when, in most Ontario towns, furniture store owners also doubled as undertakers. . . . A casket is, after all, just a piece of wooden furniture, a sort of eternal *chaise-longue*.

Kelson knew, after his first day of work, that this was for him. He had attended at the County Nursing Home with his boss Bertrand Roller to pick up a client. Kelson liked the relief that spread over waiting faces when at last the undertaker arrived. He liked the hush that surrounded the work, and he liked the money.

Kelson was a smart boy. He could see that furniture was the weak end of the business. The mark-ups were in caskets, not Formica-and-aluminum kitchen sets.

After high school Kelson went directly into the Ontario School of Undertaking in Toronto. Kelson had never been the hundred miles to Toronto before. He was impressed by how big it was, how clean it was, and how hot it got in the summer.

Kelson was also impressed by his classroom. It was the same kind of classroom in which the young Dr. Frankenstein had taken lectures. The professor stood at the front of the class, on a platform. Behind the professor was a blackboard. The students sat in an amphitheatre, at wooden desks that sloped upward from the front to the back. Kelson loved to sit high at the back of the class so that he could take in the entire scene with a swoop of his eye.

There were seventy-four students the year Kelson attended, seventy-two males and two females. Kelson often wondered whether this was natural work for women. They brought the babies into the world. Was it natural for women to help grown babies out as well? Kelson didn't know. Neither do I. Only time will tell.

After graduation Kelson went back to work full time

at Roller's Furniture. In time, Bertrand Roller retired and Kelson was there to buy the business. He had thought it through carefully. He offered Roller a price so high that even Roller himself was surprised.

Kelson went to the bank and explained his idea to Grant Simpson. It was clear to that banker's banker young Kelson didn't need the money. He only just wanted it, and a loan was quickly arranged. As soon as the deal had closed, Kelson put the furniture store, building, and inventory up for sale.

Dick Wright, who liked the furniture business but hated the funeral business, bought what Kelson had offered for sale. Kelson paid off the bank, bought a big old house that became the funeral parlour on the main floor, the mortuary in the basement, and the living quarters above all the rest.

Roger's funeral was, naturally enough, a sad affair, but it was nice to see Roger there. His open casket stood at one end of the state room. Roger never looked better.

The reception line was made up of Roger's mother, Diane, his maternal grandmother, Diane's brother, two of Diane's sisters, and Roger's two younger brothers. Where was his father when we really needed him? Where indeed.

The people of Yelton came to the funeral parlour to pay their respects. They came because they wanted to, not because they had to. They were sincere. Few, if any, sat in judgement. All were truly saddened at the loss. The people of Yelton were at their best in the face of death.

Roger's uncle shook my hand as I went through the

sad, dignified line. "Say hello to Roger," his red-eyed uncle said warmly, nodding with his head towards the open casket. I said I would, and made my way with shaky legs towards the open casket.

Roger lay with his eyes closed. He seemed relaxed, no longer afraid. He wore grey slacks, his khaki police shirt with the epaulettes on the shoulders, and a sky-blue peaked cap that said INDY 500 on it. The hat was to cover the work carried out earlier by the local coroner.

"Hi, Roger," I whispered. "What de ye know teday?" Roger said nothing, which is what I usually said. I turned to walk away, my head spinning slightly. "Good-bye, Roger," I said. "Drive carefully."

*

CROSS-COUNTRY CHECK-UP; WHERE ARE YOU CALLING FROM, PLEASE?

"Glace Bay."

"Do you think law and order in this country has broken down?"

"Sure it has."

"Why do you say that, sir?"

"I'll give you three reasons. In the first place the police don't have the power they need to act quickly or at all. If they want to get a search warrant, for example, they have to go before a judge and explain to him why they need to go in. Why take the time? For one thing, the judge only has the information that the police supply. If they can't dream up reasons enough to convince a judge who has no other information, they should be out delivering papers or, worse yet, the mail. And even if the judge does refuse the warrant, the police just have to wake up another judge and get him to sign the warrant. Tell me

this: what would the police want to go into someone else's house and snoop around for? You don't think they have enough excitement already?

Another thing . . ."

"Could you be brief, sir?"

"Certainly. Another thing is this thing of reading a person their rights. Now get this. The police say to some felon who is anxious to share what he knows that, before he tells them a thing, he has the right to call his lawyer. And you know what the lawyer tells his client: 'Don't say nothin'.' That's what the lawyer tells the guy. Don't say a thing. Don't say, 'I didn't do it,' if the guy didn't do it, and don't say, 'I did do it,' if the guy did in fact commit the crime. What is this, a TV *game show or a system of justice?"*

"Briefly, sir, your third point."

"My third point is that when they finally convict the guy, he usually gets a scolding from the judge and a finger pointing to the door. I mean, who watches these people, once they are back on the street? Nobody, that's who!"

"Thank you very much for your call . . ."

Several days after the funeral, Diane went to the police station to see Chief Shelton. "Chief," she said, "it seems strange to me, and to other people that I have talked to, that one minute my boy is out on the street, hale and hearty, and the next minute he is dead."

"Hmmm," said the Chief. His face turned red.

"Something happened here at this station," Diane went on. "And I think I have a right to know what that was!"

"You have a complaint?" The Chief asked.

"Yes," said Diane.

The Chief said nothing. He could feel himself getting angry. At the same time he felt as if he wanted to cry. He went into his back office and returned holding a sheet of paper. This is what the page said:

> TO: The Yelton Police Department,
> and to
> The Police Committee, Town of Yelton:
>
> I, ..., of the .... of .... hereby make the following complaint against the Police Force of the Town of Yelton (type or print neatly your complaint here):
>
> Dated at Yelton this ...... day of .... 198 .
>
> ....
> (sign here)

Diane had never been particularly good at expressing herself on paper or at standing up to men. She meekly took the page and headed for the door. Diane felt nauseated. Guilt, at having confronted the Chief and then submitting to him, went head to head with the feeling of rage and turned the contents of her stomach into liquid. It was the same feeling she had experienced after she had been brutalized by her father and later her husband. The fact that there were no bruises didn't make it better. She was overwhelmed by her feelings of powerlessness.

Diane quickly walked away from the police station. She wanted to gain control of herself. She was afraid she was going to cry. Her mind raced as to who might help her. Her social worker? . . . What help had I been? The police came back to mind. She crumpled the complaint form and threw it into the street. She felt dizzy and stopped walking for a moment to regain her balance. Who could help?

Her Member of Parliament? Who was he? What was his name? Where did you find him?

Diane thought of the Town Clerk. Maybe he could help. The clerk, as it turned out, was at a convention in Toronto, with the Mayor. The convention was concerned with emergency measures to be taken in case of nuclear attack and similar disasters. The budget director would later be pleased to learn that neither man had taken his wife.

Diane headed to the clerk's office. She had to go somewhere. She stood at the high counter that separated the public from the staff.

Dorothy Dundas was the deputy clerk. Dorothy was doing the work she liked best. She was calculating the penalty to be added to the accounts of property owners who hadn't paid their property taxes on time. Dorothy was just working on Lyle Flynn's tax notice. Lyle owned the local vacuum repair depot. Lyle was three years in arrears, which meant the town could legally sell his property to recover the arrears of taxes. Dorothy felt Diane's presence but went on working. She hated to be disturbed when she was working on a tax sale.

Diane waited patiently. People in small towns are taught to be patient. Finally, when Dorothy felt she had kept Diane waiting long enough, she pushed away from her desk and came towards the counter.

Dorothy was a tall woman, straight and stern. She was fifty-three and had worked for the town for thirty of those years. She might have become the town's clerk, some years back, had she been a man.

Dorothy had met her husband, Keith, on her first day of work. He had been a labourer for the public works department. Eight years ago Keith had been made foreman. He wasn't nearly as smart as his wife. He also made double the money she did, even though Dorothy's job was at least of equal value. . . . Don't blame me. I don't make the rules.

Keith Dundas hated his job, working alone. He loved to be with people. His wife Dorothy hated people. She wasn't all that crazy about Keith either.

"I want to lay a complaint against the police," Diane said to Dorothy.

"You can't do that here," Dorothy said. She saw that Diane was upset. "I would really like to help you," Dorothy added almost kindly, "but you have to go the police to complain about them."

"What's the use?" Diane asked. "The Chief will only protect his men."

Dorothy reached under the counter and pulled out a well-worn copy of a document entitled *Procedure Manual, Town of Yelton*. She impatiently thumbed through the pages until she came to the appropriate section. This is what the section said:

> COMPLAINTS:
>
> 1. AGAINST POLICE
>
> Complaints against the Town Police, or any of its members, shall be dealt with as follows:
>
> (a) A complaint must be made to the Chief of Police within 30 days of the alleged event.
>
> (b) The complaint must be submitted

in writing on an approved form, provided by the Chief of Police to the citizen wishing to make the complaint.

(c) The Chief shall have 30 days to investigate the complaint and provide a written report of his findings to the complainant, and to the Police Committee of Council.

(d) The complainant, if not satisfied with the report of the Chief, shall have 30 days from the receipt thereof to appeal the findings of the Chief. Such appeal shall be in writing, on an approved form, and delivered to the Town Clerk or his Deputy.

(e) The Police Committee of Council shall meet in camera within 60 days of receiving the appeal and shall cause a report of its findings to be prepared by the Town Clerk. The decision of the Police Committee contained in the report shall be delivered to the complainant and the Chief of Police, along with any recommendations of the Committee, including disciplinary action, if any, within 30 days of their meeting. All decisions of the Committee are final and binding upon the complainant.

Tears came to Diane's eyes. She didn't write well, but she understood a run-around.

"Want some free advice?" said Dorothy, moving back

to her tax sale. "Get yourself a lawyer. They're the only ones that can make sense of that gobbledegook."

*

CROSS-COUNTRY CHECK-UP; WHERE ARE YOU CALLING FROM, PLEASE?

"Toronto."

"Do you think the women's movement is filling its mandate?"

"No, I don't."

"Can you tell us why not, caller?"

"Well, from my own experience, it hasn't helped me one little bit. The movement seems to be run by a group of self-interested professionals, lawyers, professors, and business women. They become irate if some woman is passed over for the job of dean at a law school. I mean, really. Or how many women are vice-presidents of large corporations. To the women with the power in the women's movement, that's the big issue."

"What do you consider the big issue?"

"Unfortunately, the big issue is little people. People like me, who have never been to college. Poor single mothers, immigrant women, native women, battered women. Have you ever heard of the powerful women doing anything more than paying lip service to those problems? I doubt it."

"What seems to be the problem then?"

"The problem is that the powerful women in the women's movement have been co-opted by men. What they aspire to is the things men have at the top. . . . Have you ever been in a shelter for battered women? I have."

"Perhaps you can tell us what it's like."

"Sure. It's crowded. That's what I remember: the crowd. Women and children, who have fled from their

homes, to be crowded together, falling all over each other to take a bath or have a cup of coffee. Looking for a moment of privacy . . . waiting."

"For what?"

"Exactly. For what! Not to be made dean of a law school, that's for sure. They're waiting for emergency housing. For financial assistance that won't be enough to support them and their children. They're waiting for the opportunity to get educational upgrading that isn't there, so they can have some control over their lives. They're looking for some professional assistance to help them sort out the psychology that led them into the mess in the first place."

"Isn't the women's movement helping change all that?"

"I think there will be a woman dean long before the problems of poor women are seriously looked at."

"Thank you very much for your call."

*

MAGIC QUESTION NUMBER TWO (CONT'D):
What in fact did you end up with?

This was a hard one! What in fact did I end up with?

What in fact did you end up with?

I'll tell you what I didn't end up with, and that's for sure. I didn't end up with Leslie Caron! I didn't end up with what I thought I'd end up with.

I think my problem was that I bought the message. My mother and even my father taught me that if I was good, if I was decent, all would work out well for me.

Didn't it work out for Cary Grant and Jimmy Stewart? Didn't Gene Kelly marry Leslie Caron in *An American in Paris*? Wasn't it said of Scrooge that he kept Christmas in his heart as well as any man, and better?

Who the hell tells you when you're growing up that it isn't enough to be good and decent?

What in fact did you end up with??

Jesus! What did I end up with? A job helping people who can't be helped? A job providing people who can't be helped with services that don't exist?

Doc, do you remember when Barry Sullivan played the Catholic priest? Didn't Frank Sinatra once play a priest too?

I remember leafing through *Life* magazine as a kid. Albert Schweitzer helping the lepers; Princess Elizabeth and her darling little sister, Margaret, bringing flowers and joy to war orphans. And real-life heroes too, who rescued children from flaming tenements in New York, and policemen who risked their lives to save some kid's dog. It seemed to make a difference!

What in fact did you end up with???

Doc, do you remember how happy Princess Grace was when she married Prince Ranier? How about Robert Young and Jane Wyatt in *Father Knows Best*, and Irene Dunne in *I Remember Mama*? Did anyone ever tell you that it was all a lie? . . . They sure as hell didn't tell me.

What in fact did you end up with????

Can I ask a question?

What in fact did you end up with?????

OK, OK, I ended up with reality. I ended up with a woman who is different than me. A woman I don't really understand. Christ, sometimes I think it would have been easier if I were gay. At least I'd probably know what the other guy was thinking . . . but a woman! A woman is different. A woman's wrist, for example . . . delicate.

Her smell . . . her neck . . . her breasts . . . her laugh . . . different.

What did I end up with? Something different. Something very different.

I'll tell you the truth, Doc, I'm terrified that I'm offending some feminist. I'm a feminist, for Christ sakes . . . I'm offending myself.

To tell you the truth, I never know what a woman is thinking. I mean, how do you know unless you ARE a woman? A woman is different.

Now I have done it. I have definitely offended a feminist.

Listen, Doc, one day Faith came home from court. It must have been a lousy day. I could see she was upset. . . . You know what Faith said to me? She said, "I wish I were six feet four inches tall, with a dong ten inches long!"

God, no, Faith. Then we'd be almost the same. (I said almost, didn't I?)

OK, Doc, first and foremost, I got someone who is different.

Want some other differences?

I like order. Faith opts for chaos.

I like the bed made every day. Faith can take it or leave it.

When I cook, the dishes are washed as I use them. When Faith cooks, the kitchen looks like a demolition derby.

Is the laundry washed? . . . Sure. When we run out of clothes.

I know what you're thinking, Doc. I'm a big boy. Right? I can do the laundry myself if it means that much to me. Sure I can. But all the time? And the thing that galls me is that Faith can do all those things so much better than I. . . . Like cleaning the house. Like cooking. Like making the bed. For Christ sakes, when I went to school, boys never even took Home Ec., believe me.

What in fact did you end up with??????

Can I please just finish this thought? . . .

I understand the problem that women have in our society. I really do. I know about the injustices. I said I was a feminist. I try to help change things. You know that. But I'm beginning to wonder when I walk in the door at night . . . who I am!

I mean, what's wrong with me being just a little bit like Gene Kelly? Why can't I care for this woman? Is "romance" an anti-feminist word? If the rules have to change, can't they change just a little more slowly?

What in fact did you end up with???????

OK, OK, Doc. ***What in fact did I end up with????????***

I end up with DIFFERENCE!

I love that difference . . . I hate that difference!

*

Diane kept her appointment with Dr. Livsey. A sign on his front door commanded REMOVE YOUR BOOTS BEFORE ENTERING.

It was early October, and 22 degrees Celsius in Yelton. A second, smaller sign over a red button suggested that patients RING AND WALK IN. She did.

As Diane opened the door, she was greeted by four pairs of eyes belonging to earlier arrivals. All of them had either removed their boots before entering or left them at home. Diane looked around the room for help. A sign on a magazine table said PLEASE CHECK IN WITH RECEPTIONIST.

Diane went over to a desk behind which a pretty young woman sat. She wore the starched lab coat of a professional although she had never completed Grade Eleven typing. On the other hand, her makeup was superb.

"Diane Camp for Dr. Livsey," Diane said.

"Hmmm," said the receptionist, looking up from the form filled with little boxes that she was mangling in her typewriter. She paused for a moment and looked Diane over before delivering history's biggest lie: "The doctor will be with you in a moment!"

Diane looked away and thought, "Bitch."... It is amazing how much power a little makeup and a lab coat can give. Diane turned toward the four pairs of already-seated eyes, which were checking to make sure that nobody got in before them.

"Christ," thought Diane, "where can I sit?" Her eyes quickly swept the room. She was looking for three more signs that should have been hung around the room. The signs would have read:

TERMINALLY ILL . . . SIT HERE
MOTHERS WITH CHILDREN . . . SIT HERE
HEALTHY PATIENTS . . . SIT HERE

She went to the magazine table to stall for time before choosing a spot. The table held a pile of out-of-date magazines. All of them appeared to harbour death-dealing microbes planted by former readers. Diane reached for a copy of *Canadian Physician*. This was the perfect choice. It featured holidays in exotic and exciting locales that a doctor could afford, and which the doctor could write off as a business expense. It also contained all sorts of wonderfully colourful drug ads.

Diane found a seat between an elderly man who appeared to be suffering from nothing worse than old age and a teenage girl who looked as if she were waiting for an allergy shot. Diane put the magazine in her lap and promptly fell asleep.

"Diane Camp," a voice called. Diane was immediately awake. "This way, please," an efficient voice called out. Diane got up without thinking. The magazine on her lap fell to the floor, sending the dozing microbes jumping and skipping like a family of fleas in all directions. Diane left the *Canadian Physician* where it fell.

A tall woman in a nurse's uniform led Diane to one of the four cubicles that were situated behind the door that separated the waiting room from the doctor. Curtains on tracks separated the cubicles so that the patients could have the illusions of privacy.

Diane's cubicle contained an old black examining table with a sheet of white paper. The white paper was on a roller at the foot of the table. The idea was to change the paper after each patient, to keep one patient's microbes off the next patient. Diane noticed a wrinkle in the paper and wondered if it had been changed.

"Hop up on the table," the tall woman said.

"I'm here to speak to the doctor about something, not to be examined, Nurse," Diane said.

Actually, the tall woman was Sarah Oates. Her husband, Bing, owned the local GM dealership, Oates Motors. Sarah had been a self-taught chiropodist who had scoured the calluses off the troubled feet of Dr. Livsey's wife so successfully that she had insisted the doctor hire Sarah as his assistant.

The doctor had taught Sarah to take blood and correctly keep track of the hundreds of sample bottles of urine that were collected during a week. He also showed her how to run routine lab tests and report the findings to him. Combined with her foot experience and subsequent training, Sarah Oates could be called "nurse" . . . sort of.

"Dr. Livsey likes to see the patients in here first," Sarah said kindly but firmly.

Diane was aware of the other three curtain-clad cubicles. "I'm not a patient, like, right now, Nurse," she whispered.

"I know," Sarah replied warmly. "The doctor will be with you in a moment," she lied, and swished the cubicle curtain closed behind her.

Sarah was quite right to place Diane in a cubicle. The doctor had given those very instructions to her, regardless of who came in. Even hapless drug salesmen found themselves ordered to hop up on the examining table by the efficient Sarah Oates.

Dr. Livsey had developed this regimen as a result of a seminar he had attended in Las Vegas several years back. The doctor had read about the lecture/gambling junket in a direct-mail piece, sent to all members of the Canadian Medical Association.

The piece had said in part:

> DOCTORS DESERVE BIG BUCKS!
>
> No longer do Canadian Doctors have to feel guilty about providing first-class health care and receiving first-class remuneration. It's no sin to be paid . . . WELL . . . for what you do!
>
> NOW, American Doctors and others share their business strategy with you in this first-ever lecture/fun junket seminar, sponsored by THE CANADIAN DOCTOR FINANCIAL ADVISORY GROUP.
>
> Dr. Oliver M. Goldblum, renowned general practitioner of Houston, Texas, shares his secrets with you on how he turned his family practice from a gross of $175,000 a year into MORE THAN THREE TIMES THAT FIGURE, while increasing his efficiency, and leisure time too!
>
> Sir Edwin Heathcote, M.D., FRSA diagnostic surgeon, St. Hilda's Infirmary, Great Britain, shows how efficient office and patient management can make huge profits EVEN IN STATE-RUN HEALTH-CARE PLANS!!
>
> It's no sin to be paid justly for what you do. We at THE ADVISORY GROUP want the opportunity to show you how *your life-giving work can increase your life-savings potential!*
>
> Join us for this tax-deductible seminar series in exciting Las Vegas this February, for work session by day and relaxation by night.

Dr. Livsey never regretted that junket, even though it cost him an additional $1,200 US during relaxation time.

Dr. Livsey heard the renowned Dr. Oliver M. Goldblum deliver the speech that had in fact contributed in no small measure to his renown as well as to his annual gross income. The speech, in its shortened version, went like this:

> "You all probably heard the one about the Greek immigrant who went to his attorney because he wanted to change his name from Nicholas Poppouloppolis to Nick Poppouloppolis. His attorney told him that he could indeed have his name changed, but it would cost him $1,500.
>
> "The immigrant was insistent, and some time later found himself in front of a judge, who made the order changing his name to Nick Poppouloppolis.
>
> " 'Tell me one thing,' said the judge. 'Why would you spend $1,500 to have your first name changed to Nick?'
>
> " 'Well,' says Nick to the judge, 'on the one hand, nobody calls me Nicholas . . . they just call me Nick, so I change it to Nick. On the other hand, nobody uses my last name Poppouloppolis because they can't pronounce it, so there is no reason to change it.'
>
> "There you have it, Doctors. People aren't interested in names they can't pronounce. When a patient comes to his doctor, he doesn't want a lot of fancy medical talk; he just wants one of three things:
>
> "A prescription,
> A clean bill of health, or

A referral to a specialist.

"Remember this, Doctors: Health insurance plans, public or private, don't pay by the hour. They pay by the procedure. You get paid just as much for a three-minute consultation as for a sixty-minute consult.

"You get paid just the same if you take the blood pressure or one of your girls takes the blood pressure. And you don't get paid at all if you're sitting around the office waiting for your ten-o'clock appointment to show.

"Doctors, never have fewer than eight appointments at the same time. . . . That's what I said, EIGHT . . . four in the examining room and four in the waiting room.

"The four in the waiting room don't mind because they only see a maximum of three in front of them. And the four in the examining rooms don't mind either because your girl will always be two ahead of you, doing simple but lucrative procedures while you are busy diagnosing, prescribing, or referring in the other two cubicles.

"Doctors [Oliver M. Goldblum said, raising his hands towards the heavens], it's time to break the old stereotype of the good but poor country doctor. Today you don't just deliver babies. Today, good Doctors, you deliver HEALTH SERVICES.

"Think of your place of business, not as a doctor's office, a place of nostrums and pharmacopoeia, but as a plant, with a line that starts in your waiting room and ends at the billing desk, a line serviced by you and your staff, a line that delivers health services.

"And, finally, those people in the line who seek

> your services, your professional opinion, your divine, life-giving touch . . . think of those people along the line lovingly as product. Then, Doctors, you can be truly efficient, not only for your own good, but for the good of the product you were meant to serve!
>
> "Believe me, Doctors . . . it works for me!"

Diane sat on the examining table, alone, and tried to find something to distract her. The weight scale and height-measurement apparatus, the old blood pressure gauge, the stainless steel tray that held stainless steel instruments, and the packages of gauze were all there. She could hear murmuring from other cubicles, something about bowels, but not enough to know whose they were or what the problem was.

Suddenly the curtain was thrown aside and in strode Dr. Livsey. He was in his mid-fifties, short, balding, and overweight. He wore half-glasses over which he peered. The glasses did not hide his pallid complexion, the blue circles under his eyes, or the cilia-like hairs that protruded from his nostrils. He wore a white crisp starched lab coat that covered a greyish shirt that had once been white, as well as baggy grey wool pants. A stethoscope hung from his neck. . . . He looked every inch a doctor.

Dr. Livsey looked at Diane without recognition.

"I'm Diane Camp," she said, almost in a whisper. The doctor continued to look at Diane uncertainly. She had, after all, been his patient for only fifteen years. "Roger Camp's mother," she spoke up.

Nothing. Still blank.

"The boy you did the report on after he was . . . found."

At last, recognition. "Mrs. Camp," Dr. Livsey said, as if he had known all along who she was, "I'm truly sorry for your loss." Dr. Livsey meant it too. Tears sprang into Diane's eyes. The doctor felt slightly overcome himself. He looked at the inappropriate setting, he standing in front of the open curtain, Diane perched on the examining table.

"What would Oliver M. Goldblum do?" he wondered. Dr. Livsey imagined his waiting room filling up with product as well as the examining room occupied by partially clad men and women. If he broke the line now, he would pay for it for the rest of the day, in more ways than one. "Come into my office," he said kindly and led the way past waving curtains.

Dr. Livsey's office was decorated by the same designer who had created the examining rooms. Falling plaster had been covered over with sheets of plywood, coloured to look like burled oak. His desk had been bought at an auction held by the Province of Ontario, Ministry of Supply, some twenty-five years earlier, when the government of the day had sold all of its least attractive and most-used office equipment. He had paid $20 for the desk and $40 for a desk chair. The walls were brightened by a colourful calendar selling pills for gout, as well as by Dr. Livsey's class picture, consisting of eighty-seven tiny heads, each in its own little oval, and four diplomas and degrees, all with large red official seals.

Dr. Livsey was living proof that most doctors love to make money but hate to spend it, except on themselves. . . . Show me a really nice doctor's office and I'll show you a doctor of chiropractic!

The two sat down, each on his and her own side of

the used government desk. "Something very strange is going on, Doctor," Diane said. "No one will tell me anythin' about how my son came to be dead."

This piece of news frightened the doctor. "Oh?" he said.

"Yes," said Diane, mistaking his "Oh?" for interest. "I've been to the police. They won't tell me anythin', and they won't do anythin' either. I've also been to the Town Hall. They suggested I see a lawyer. I wanted to speak to you first because you're the coroner, to sort of get your help, and then I'm going to a lawyer."

"Oh?" Dr. Livsey repeated. At the mention of the word "lawyer," Dr. Livsey became more ashen, if that was possible.

"Yes," said Diane, still mistaking the doctor's response for interest. "I want to get to the bottom of my son's death." Tears again filled Diane's eyes, this time more from grief than from gratitude. Dr. Livsey pushed a box of single-ply, no-name tissues towards Diane. His eyes filled with humanity as he looked upon the sobbing mother.

"I haven't finished my report, and so it's hard to tell you much." He paused. "I'm not sure the information would do you much good anyhow." . . . Pause. . . . "It is, after all, quite technical." . . . Pause. . . . "Quite complex." . . . Pause. . . . "The information is inconclusive anyhow." . . . Pause. . . . "There are no answers here!"

Dr. Livsey said all this as if he were confiding some cosmic secret to an infant. He looked at Diane closely to see if she had understood. "If I were you," he went on, "I'd let the authorities handle it. I know you're suffering pain over this tragic loss. My prescription for you is to try and get over it as fast as you can. Don't prolong your grief. Life is tough enough, Diane. Believe me, I know what I'm talking about. . . . I'm a doctor."

*

People I speak to are always complaining about their doctors. What the hell do they expect from a poor M.D.? Half the time doctors don't know what the problem is and the rest of the time they are afraid to share the information because they might be wrong. Believe me, I know what I'm talking about. . . . I'm a Ph.D. in social work.

*

Did you hear the one about the announcer at the Saddledome Arena who asked over the PA if there was a doctor in the house . . . and everyone stood up? . . .

*

To tell you the truth, I understand Dr. Livsey, I really do. People I work with always think I have all the answers too. Jesus, we're only human. Because I give advice to others, it doesn't mean that I have all the answers or that my life isn't in a complete shambles.

What difference does that make? And whose business is it anyhow how I screw up my life?

Take my marriage counsellor, for example. I don't know the first damn thing about her, whether she's married or living with someone, or what.

To tell you the truth, she is a very attractive woman, I'd say about thirty-five, with very long legs, sheathed in smoky grey nylons, that are always in motion. You know, crossing and uncrossing. She doesn't have any rings on her fingers. No jewellery at all. She has never made the slightest reference to her private life . . . nor have I heard anything about her from anyone else in the profession whom I've asked. Like I say, it isn't any of my damn business.

Which is exactly the point. While she may appear to know all the answers, crossing and uncrossing those smoky, long, lovely legs, I know damn well she doesn't. And it isn't fair to expect that she should. . . . She is, after all, just human.

*

Police Chief Shelton knew that Diane was making enquiries. So did his constables. They weren't worried. Why should they be? It wasn't the first complaint. The complaint procedure had never let them down before. There was no reason to believe it would now.

Constable Smyth had never mentioned it to his wife, Bea. Why should he? Smyth had never talked about his work before. There was no reason to believe he would now.

In fact, Smyth rarely talked to anyone except his fellow officers. That's the way it is in police work. Others wouldn't understand anyhow.

Smyth did notice recently, however, that he was talking to things. On the beat he would talk to familiar objects, like the hydrant at the corner of Randall and Wiseman. "Everything under control here?" he would ask. The hydrant sat solid. "Yeah," Smyth would agree.

At the corner of Gloucester and Deloraine to a notch on the telephone pole that he imagined was a secret sensor: "Anything to report?" The secret sensor hummed its message to the peace officer. "Hmmm," said Smyth.

Smyth had two children, a boy sixteen and a daughter twelve. The kids were used to being ignored. They thought that's how fathers were, and Bea, his wife, had become a closet alcoholic long ago. None of them thought it strange when Smyth questioned the stereo or joked with the fridge.

Smyth himself seemed unaware of his preference for things over people. It seemed natural enough to him. Things seemed to understand him, and no thing had ever betrayed his confidence.

People, on the other hand, were unreliable. Nobody told him the truth, not the town doctor, not the town drunk. The world was made up of lying scum.

Q: *How fast were you going?*
A: About thirty!
Q: *Have you had anything to drink?*
A: One, maybe two . . . about an hour ago!
Q: *Did you pay for those pantyhose?*
A: Honest, I forgot I had them!

It didn't seem to interfere with his work either. As he got out of his police cruiser, after having stopped a motorist, he would ask his radar unit, "How fast was that sucker going? . . . Fifteen over the limit, eh?"

He had always trusted his equipment, the police car, the two-way radio, his night-stick.

On the night that Roger had died mysteriously, Smyth had mentioned to his night-stick that Roger claimed he was just out enjoying the evening air. "Can you believe that shit?" Smyth asked his old ebony friend.

CHAPTER THREE

*

Diane kept her appointment with Faith. She entered the recently renovated former warehouse and was directed by an efficient receptionist to the waiting area. It was richly decorated in ice greys and dusky blues. Schumacher wallpaper in a fine, small pattern covered the walls, and grey wool carpets covered the finished oak board planks. Magazines were placed on an antique oak table. A large Chinese lamp illuminated the area. Grey, blue, and delicate pink dragons wound around the base of the lamp. "Christ," thought Diane as she sank into the blue-grey leather sofa, "this place is better than my living room."

Here was a difference between doctors and lawyers. Doctors love to make money but hate to spend it on anyone except themselves. Lawyers love to spend money on everything . . . even if sometimes the money isn't their own.

Here's another difference: lawyers take the time to listen to their clients, sometimes for hours. Maybe that's because lawyers are paid by the hour, not the procedure. I don't know.

In her interview with Faith, Diane told Faith a bit about her own life. Faith took it all down with a pink Cross pen on ice-blue notepaper.

This is what she said:

> "My parents married shortly before I was born. My mother, Iris, was eighteen. My father, Steve, was eighteen too. My dad didn't have a job. Mom worked in the local meat-processing plant. Her job was to gut turkeys as they came by, hanging

upside down by their scrawny yellow turkey feet, on a conveyor belt that travelled past the gutters at eye level. Mom hated to give up that job. Dad hated to give up his bachelorhood. Both families had insisted my parents get married. I'm told several guests cried at the small family wedding. Some even cried at mine.

"It turned out that my father, like his father before him, hated to work but loved to drink. He also loved to come home, all pissed up, and beat up on my mom and me. It was in these early years I learned to keep my head down and to say Yes . . . and Yes . . . and Yes! . . . At the age of five I also learned to stroke my father's penis and rub his sperm on his tummy. As Maurice Chevalier once said, 'Thank heaven for little girls.'

"Steve disappeared when I was eight. I heard he got drunk and fell off Balls Bridge fishing for river trout one spring morning. No one reported him missing and nobody in Yelton ever saw him again.

"Iris never had a steady beau after that. She raised me and my two brothers out of the proceeds of part-time jobs and welfare.

"I met Roger's father at a dance, at the Yelton and District Community Centre. Roger's father, Arnold, was famous in Yelton for his lip-synch imitations of Elvis Presley. Jesus, I couldn't take my eyes off his hip synch. He was really good. Roger was conceived one night on my bed when mom was out at the local hotel. I was eighteen; so was Arnold. Both families insisted we get married. . . . History has a funny way of repeating itself.

"Roger's dad hung around for only two years. During that time he discovered that married life wasn't for him, that being a father held no special interest, and that selling dope to an undercover agent gets you eighteen months' reformatory time.

"Fortunately, Roger's dad never really did come back for any length of time. A couple of times he showed up and did his Elvis lip-and-hip-synch thing for me, but generally the next morning he was gone.

"By the time Roger turned four, Arnold was serving five years in Kingston. At the trial a cop told the judge that Arnold had laced the heroin with arsenic. Arnold was no dummy . . . he had a hunch the guy was a narc."

Diane had never bothered to remarry or even to divorce. She had given birth to two more boys by different fathers and had for the most part lived on welfare and Mother's Allowance. Now Legal Aid undertook to pay her legal expenses and Faith undertook to find out how her son had died.

Some people in my line of work burn out, or so they say. To tell you the truth, I don't see it that way. I think they just give up . . . quit. Not me!

What they forget, the quitters, is that it took two million years of evolution to get us this far. Viewed in that light, Diane Camp was making steady progress. It's true, it appeared to Diane that her son Roger had been beaten to death, but no one was hitting on Diane Camp anymore. And if she had had a daughter, there's no way she would have allowed that girl to marry just because she was pregnant.

*

After Diane left, Faith picked up a microphone and dictated the following letter:

TO: Crown Attorney,
The Court House,
The Square,
Goderich, Ontario

Dear Sir:

RE: Roger Camp

We have been retained by Diane Camp, mother of the above-mentioned who died under mysterious circumstances on or about the 27th day of October, 1987. You will recall that Roger Camp, was found dead shortly after being released from the custody of the Yelton Police.

Ms. Camp informs me that she requested the Chief of the Yelton police force to carry out a full investigation as to the cause of death; however, to the best of our knowledge, no such investigation has been carried out.

We would be obliged if you could assist our client by providing us with a full report as to the nature of any injuries sustained, the cause of such injuries, and the nature of criminal charges, if any, laid as a result thereof.

We look forward to your reply and in

anticipation, we thank you for your kind co-operation.
Yours very truly,

Faith also wrote to Dr. Livsey, who was also the County Coroner, requesting the medical report he had refused to provide to her client.

*

CROSS-COUNTRY CHECK-UP; WHERE ARE YOU CALLING FROM, PLEASE?

"Calgary."

"Is our social welfare system working?"

"In a pig's eye! The system works for one group of people, and they don't need for nothin'."

"Which group are you referring to, sir?"

"The people who run the bloody system, that's who. They get paid whether people are getting enough welfare or not. And lookit. There needs to be two groups of people the system serves: the losers and the survivors. Let's stop fooling ourselves; there are people out there who do diddly-squat, and that's what they should get. Bare necessities. And their kids are going to be no damn better, so don't waste the money. Don't let them kid you; some people don't want the cycle of poverty broken, especially the people who run the bloody boondoggle.

"On the other hand, some people just need support, some money to take care of them and their kids till they get a job or schooling or whatever. Give them what it takes for a year or two. Let the people decide: are they dross or do they want to work their asses off like the rest of us? Let's have two lines at welfare . . . losers, line up here . . . temporary support, here.

"Let's stop holding hands. Accept the losers for what

they are and give them what they deserve. For the rest, help 'em out. Maybe we can start saving some money and get rid of the social-worker, bureaucrat hangers-on that suck as much from the system as the losers do."

"Thank you for expressing your view."

"Don't mention it!"

CHAPTER FOUR

I NEVER REALLY FELT TOTALLY COMFORTABLE WITH our marriage counsellor. The legs were one thing—crossing at the knee and recrossing onto the other knee. The black, fine wool, just-below-the-knee-high skirt. That didn't help either.

I would have been a whole lot happier, too, if she had worn a blouse other than the cream pure silks she preferred. Sometimes they were buttoned to the neck and sometimes opened two or three buttons, depending on the blouse, but always high-gloss, shimmering silk. I don't have to tell you what shimmered!

Faith, of course, would not have been distracted . . . not in the same way anyhow. Is that an advantage one female feminist would give to another female feminist over a male feminist? . . . How could you possibly know?

I know, I know, women have been going to male doctors and marriage counsellors for years. . . . Did that give a male bias to the proceedings? . . . Well, did it? . . . I wouldn't say no.

OK, so there have been some inequities over the years. Is this my fault? Am I doomed to live in some Sophoclean drama and suffer for the sins of my father at the hands of a butch enemy goddess? I love this woman and I'm made to feel guilty . . . for what? Caring? Concern? Being supportive?

Lookit, my wife's a lawyer. She probably makes $125,000 a year. Face it, despite my doctorate, I'm a social worker. I make $27,700, plus medical, dental, and drug care plans. I also have a hell of a pension plan. But when you get down to it, Faith is a lawyer and I'm a social worker.

When we go to parties, do you think that I don't know I'm being measured against Faith?

> *"So, what do you do?"*
> "I'm a social worker for Children's Aid."
> *"Really. That must be interesting work. Isn't your wife the lawyer?"*
> "Yes, to both questions!"
> *"Nice talking to you."*

I have never mentioned this to Faith, not once. Why should I? What can she do about it? And who gives a damn anyhow? The guys are mostly lawyers. Lawyers are probably the most aggressive, smug, and opinionated group you ever want to meet. . . . (Another difference between doctors and lawyers: doctors are smug, opinionated, and dull!)

Faith, on the other hand, complains about my spending. I admit I do like nice things, and we can afford a lot of them. But Faith, with the cheque-book, writing down, reconciling, balancing. I sometimes wonder who owns who!

You want to know one of the reasons I spend so much money? So that Faith can see I don't hold it against her that she's a lawyer and makes more than I do. Really. How many guys do you know who would be so uptight about taking money from A WOMAN? Not me. . . . God bless equal opportunity in the workplace!

I sometimes wish I had raised that point in our sessions with the marriage counsellor. But to tell you the truth, I thought, what's the point? Do you really think they would have understood?

I probably should have said a whole lot more in there, but I'm not convinced it would have made a difference. . . . "WHAT DID YOU END UP WITH?". . . Is that a fair question? How about "What might you have ended up with?" or "What did your mother end up with?" or "What did Eva Braun end up with?" . . . Christ, it's so easy to pick.

When I got married, I thought it was happily ever after. I really did. I even said so to our counsellor at one of the last sessions. I guess, when the counsellor asked me in the beginning what I thought I was getting, I should have said: "And they all lived happily ever after." . . . You think that's too much to ask?

*

"Do you want to see a movie tonight?"

"Geez, honey, not really, not tonight."

"Do you want to see a movie tonight?"

"Not if it's going to be depressing like the last one."

"Do you want to see a movie tonight?"

"Which one?"

"Do you want to take your car or mine?"

"You decide."

"Do you want me to let you off in front of the theatre?"

"No, I'll walk with you, but let's not park fourteen blocks away like last time, OK?"

"Do you want me to wait in line?"
"Why didn't we leave ten minutes earlier, like I wanted to?'

"How about these two seats over here?"
"Sure, but I'd prefer over there."

"Did you like the movie?"
"Loved it. You?"
"Yup."

*

Faith's letter landed on the Crown Attorney's desk the next day. "Make my day," the Crown Attorney hissed to himself as he read the letter.

A woman the Crown had been trying to pick up in a bar had once told him he looked like Clint Eastwood. Like all things, there had been some truth in what she said. The resemblance was in the eyes, dark brown, cold, and mean.

The Crown Attorney otherwise looked more like Walt Disney's elephant, Dumbo. Maynard Arnup was short, with pink flesh, large ears, thin curly blond hair, and a melon belly. It was the eyes that caught the attention of the woman at the bar. It was the gourd-like gut that kept them apart. At thirty-seven, Maynard Arnup was still waiting for Miss Right.

Arnup reached for a cigarette-sized cigar and clenched it between his teeth. He lit up, put his feet on the desk, and leaned back in his swivel chair. Maynard Arnup wore Ralph Lauren cowboy boots. If you had looked down at Maynard Arnup's boots from Maynard's perspective, crossed casually at the ankle, on his desk, you would have sworn it was Clint Eastwood. Maynard re-read Faith's letter.

"OK, bitch," he mumbled to himself, and flipped Faith's letter towards the desk. It hit the edge and fluttered towards the floor.

*

I wonder sometimes why anyone would want to be a crown attorney. I mean, can you imagine choosing a profession whose primary target is to put people behind bars? Wouldn't that make getting up in the morning something to look forward to?

The crown attorney, in our system, is the Queen's representative in criminal matters. Each day from sea to shining sea, the Queen's representatives flock to our courts of justice to deal with rapists and murderers and thieves and drunk drivers. It's no wonder you rarely see the Queen smiling. This is pretty seamy stuff. God Save Our Gracious Queen, and if I might add, her crown attorneys. It's dirty work, and someone's got to do it.

On the other side of the counsel table sits defence counsel. Like Faith, their duty is to do for their clients what the clients would do for themselves, had they the knowledge and training of a lawyer. Pretty lofty, eh? Know any guilty people who want to go to jail?

Wouldn't that make getting up in the morning something to look forward to . . . getting off some rapist or murderer or the like?

You think this has anything to do with justice? Hey, give me a break, OK?

*

Maynard was not amused by Faith's letter. Maynard had to work with the police every day of his life. It was the police, after all, who supplied the little Crown with his day's work. You hate to bite the hand that feeds you. Maynard looked up from his desk into the eyes of a scowling Queen whose picture adorned his wall. "Bitch," he mumbled and picked up the microphone attached to his dictating machine and fired off a letter to Chief Shelton. This is what the tape recorded:

TO: Sheldon Shelton,
Chief of Police,
Main Street,
Yelton, Ontario
N1A 2K0.

Dear Chief Shelton:

RE: Roger Camp

Enclosed herewith please find copy of letter received by me this day from the solicitor for the mother of the above-noted deceased party. I would appreciate your comments.

Yours truly,
Maynard Arnup,
Crown Attorney
encl.

*

The Chief had called his men together in their windowless little interrogation/meeting room and read Faith's letter to them. Smoke swirled around the light bulb in the green metal lampshade. The men sat. Silent. Nobody moved. Not a muscle.

Chief Shelton broke the silence. "Who was in the room when Camp was questioned?"

Smyth, Bowles, Roose, and Fitkin raised their hands.

"Who else was in the room?"

"No one," the men said in unison.

Chief Shelton got up. The investigation was over.

*

The Chief immediately went back to his office to reply to the little Crown's letter. He thought to himself, as he fumbled with the set-up on his typewriter, about the good old days in his yellow squad car in Toronto and about his longing for big crime in Yelton. Shel Shelton recognized the aura of a headache on its way. "Christ," he thought, "when the gods want to punish you, they do answer your prayers!"

Here is exactly what the Chief wrote to the Crown Attorney:

TO: Maynard Arnup,
Crown Attorney,
The Court House,
The Square,
Goderich, Ontario

Dear Sir:

RE: Roger Camp

I received your letter concerning the above-mentioned subject. I accordingly carried out a full investigation in order to ascertain if any of the force had information.

The results of the investigation have proved to be negative. Any mishap which might have befallen the subject occurred after his release from our care.

I trust this information has been of some help.

Yours truly,
S Shelton, Chief

*

Chief Shelton wasn't the only one to hold a meeting. Faith arranged to have all the Motleys, who were at the four corners when Roger was taken away, meet in her office.

They arrived as a group of nine . . . there was, for Motleys, safety in numbers. Their clothes, which appeared so brazen on the street corner, looked sad in the light of more elegant surroundings. Their skin looked sallow, their hair, which on the street looked wild and vital, was dirty, limp, and unkempt. They looked like poor kids, very young, poor, and pathetic kids.

The four-corners bravado was gone too. They giggled like nervous teens and tried to act as if they were very much at home. Faith's secretary led the Motleys into the boardroom with its large oak table and leather-covered chairs that easily accommodated the gaggle of nine. Faith sat at the head of the table and patiently took the group's names and particulars. She asked each one in the group what he or she had seen. All had seen more or less the same things: the arrival of the police, the departure of Roger. No one had seen violence.

Faith asked the witnesses if they had picked up anything from the grapevine, heard anything on the street . . . facts, rumours, anything. Nobody had.

Faith asked if anyone had a theory as to how Roger had died. Nothing.

After an hour and a half Faith called the meeting to an end. All the Motleys made for the door, including Linda Nadler. Linda was a slight girl of fourteen. She was five feet, two inches tall, weighed eighty-five pounds, had short blond hair and blue eyes.

Linda had a tiny waist and always wore skin-tight blue jeans. The jeans were so tight that she was unable to wear underwear under the jeans. As a result she wore tampons seven days a week, fifty-two weeks of the year. This constant insertion in her anatomy had resulted in a chronic vaginal infection that caused continuous discomfort. Linda thought it was worth the look. She may have been right about that.

Linda dawdled as the group made their way to the door. She made sure she was the last to leave. "Rumours," Linda whispered as she passed Faith at the door.

"Pardon?" whispered Faith.

"Maybe it was the telephone book," Linda whispered.

"Telephone book?" Faith repeated.

"Yeah," said Linda, "the Toronto telephone book!"

*

Faith's father was a chartered accountant in Regina. He was a pretty interesting guy, for a chartered accountant. He had been kind to Faith in a distant sort of way. On a scale of good, better, best, Faith had been given the better of everything by her father. He was a man who worked hard, quietly, and made his money work for him.

Faith's mom, to me, was someone who could have, in another life, been Betty Crocker. She was a kind woman who supported her husband, raised the children, and always had something of a baked-goods nature rising in the oven.

Faith told our counsellor she had anticipated that after we were married I would have become more like her father: focused, kind, and good with dough. As it turns out, I am good with dough, and with pasta too. . . . Hey, one out of three ain't bad.

To tell you the truth, I thought that Faith would be a little bit more like my mom: forgiving, conciliatory, and neat. I think it fair to say that neither of us got exactly what we bargained for . . . ah well, as Faith might say, *caveat emptor*!

I think if I ever do it again, look to become committed I mean, I will place an ad in the "Companions" section of the *Toronto Star* classified:

> Cute, male, nonsmoking professional Caucasian, fortyish, wishes to meet gorgeous feminist, thirty-threeish, to share equally domestic duties, social awareness, candlelight dinners, and intimate moments.
>
> If you are conciliatory, forgiving, and neat and want support and guidance from a sincere and caring heterosexual, write in confidence, enclosing recent photo, to Box 133, Yelton, Ontario. N1A 2K0. No triflers please.

*

Maynard Arnup liked Faith. He was, after all, a man and she was a woman. The fact that they were both lawyers didn't hurt. Maynard found the combination erotic. He looked forward to his meeting with Faith.

Faith wore a dark blue silk Alfred Sung dress, blue-black Ferragamo shoes with a two-inch heel, and carried a Cartier briefcase. Maynard greeted her in his three-piece blue suit and Ralph Lauren boots. Faith smelled faintly of Opium. Maynard smelled faintly of stale cigar.

"I want to review the Camp case," Faith said.

"That fuckin' dog," Maynard said suggestively.

"Ah, yeah," Faith answered.

Maynard thought the reply contained a faintly positive signal. "What have you got?" Maynard asked provocatively.

"This," Faith said, opening her briefcase and pulling out a file. She handed a letter from the file to Maynard.

"What's this?" Maynard asked.

"Coroner's report, prepared by Dr. Livsey."

"Right," said Maynard. Maynard read it over. "What does it mean?"

"It means that Roger Camp died of an embolism, an explosion of blood in his head."

"Right," said Maynard. "Anything about cracking of the skull? Anything about abrasions on the scalp, anything about blood in the hair?"

"Not a word," agreed Faith.

"You know what you got here then," said Maynard. "Diddly!"

"Wrong," said Faith. "I got me a Toronto telephone book."

"Good," said Maynard. "Get yourself the number of the Clarke Institute."

"Listen, Maynard," said Faith, calmly, "say two guys hold someone down. Say one guy lays a Toronto telephone book on that someone's head, and say a fourth guy hits that someone with a club right on the old telephone book. Do you know what would happen to that someone's head?"

Maynard looked at Faith.

"Shock waves is what happens, Maynard. No cracking of the skull, no abrasions to the scalp, no blood in the hair. But if someone, say a cop, hits the telephone book with an ebony night-stick often enough, and hard enough, there's a massive explosion in the head, caused by shock waves."

"Jesus," said Maynard. "Where did you get that one?"

"Reliable source," Faith said.

"OK, babe, where's the telephone book?"

"That's what I need you for, Maynard," Faith said. "I need you to apply, as Crown Attorney, for a search warrant, and I need that warrant executed by some police force other than Yelton's finest!"

"What else you got?" asked Maynard.

"This," said Faith, pulling another report from her file. "It's a letter from Wayne Grace, M.D., doctor of forensic medicine at the crime lab in Toronto. Grace says this first report, prepared by the coroner, is as consistent with the telephone-book theory as with any other explanation."

"What are you, one of the Hardy Boys?" Maynard asked.

"Nope," chirped Faith. "I'm their missing mother!"

*

Ahhh! That's my Faith. Make 'em sit up and take note, girl! Get out o' her way.

Can you imagine. Far from Leslie Caron, I ended up with the divine Katharine Hepburn straight out of *Adam's Rib*. You remember that one. She's a lawyer, her husband, Spencer Tracy, is a district attorney, and they go head to head in a courtroom? . . . You can get it on video.

The divine Katharine Hepburn had children in that movie. They were all grown up. Remember? Katharine talks to one of them briefly on the telephone, from her hotel room. The kid probably attended Wellesley

College or Yale or somewhere Ivy League. Ah, that Katharine Hepburn. Somehow she found the time to have kids. Did I mention to you that Faith and I don't have any? Children, I mean. I think we could find the time.

Tell me the truth: do you think the divine Katharine Hepburn suffered from "Impostor Syndrome"? . . . Faith did. I'm not kidding. Faith didn't think she was really a lawyer. Do you know what I mean?

She said that on some days she felt as if she was only just pretending to be a lawyer and that all the judges and all the male lawyers knew it. . . . Do you think it was too much adolescent exposure to *Sixteen* magazine? I'll be darned if I know.

My own guess is that Katharine Hepburn didn't suffer from "Impostor Syndrome" because it hadn't been isolated in those early years.

Faith has a friend who strips film for a firm that makes colour separations for magazines. Ironically, her name is Katharine too.

Katharine the stripper is a big, big feminist. She is constantly complaining that she has to strip ads for car wax companies and vacation resorts that use partially clad women to sell their products. She claims it makes her physically ill.

Katharine the stripper says that women have been objectified, that our society doesn't think of them as people but as receptacles for male fantasies. She may be right about that.

I once made the mistake of leafing through a *Life* magazine while Katharine the stripper was visiting with Faith. I never thought of *Life* magazine as being particularly pornographic, but in one sense I guess you'd have to say it was.

The issue I was thumbing through, even ignoring the car wax and vacation ads, featured a woman figure skater. I don't suppose I need to tell you what she was wearing. I wanted to ask Katharine the stripper if she thought the skater could do a triple axel in a long dress, but I didn't want to get into an argument with one of Faith's friends.

Can I tell you something, off the record? For years I have wanted to buy a copy of *High Society*, just to see what's inside. Do you know what I mean? Frankly, I'm too embarrassed to take it up to the cash. . . . My guess is I will die wondering.

Katharine the stripper is a very attractive woman herself. A very voluptuous five feet, nine inches, with natural blond shoulder-length hair, a full figure, soft hot skin, and a creamy complexion that requires no makeup. Easy for her to be critical. To her credit, Katharine the stripper is also the only woman I know who still wears a muumuu.

Thank you, Katharine, for raising my consciousness. I've cancelled my subscription to *Life*, *Maclean's*, and *Chatelaine* and replaced them with *Ranger Rick* and *Commentary*.

In a way, if you want to know the truth, I resent having to give up those ads. They seem harmless enough, but I understand if we are going to deal with the problem of "Impostor Syndrome," then women are, at least for their own good, going to have to stop acting like objects of our heart's desire, and start acting and posing like real people. . . . I think some pimple ads are already sending the message.

*

Five days after Faith's meeting with Maynard Arnup, at approximately three-thirty in the afternoon, a black-

and-white cruiser, with the letters OPP marked on the door, pulled up to the Yelton Police Station. A friendly-looking cop named Hall got out. He held a piece of paper with a red seal affixed to it. It was a search warrant.

Inside the station, a constable by the name of Smyth was on duty. He was sitting in front of a typewriter and talking to it as he prepared the occurrence sheet for the previous day.

Hall entered the station and slipped through a gate in the counter that divided the public from their law enforcement officers.

"I have a search warrant," Hall said to Smyth, handing him the document.

Smyth didn't look up and repeated to his typewriter, "He has a warrant."

"Ah, yeah. We're looking for a Toronto telephone book, here at the station. You know where it's kept?"

"What the fuck do you want with a Toronto telephone book?" Smyth asked. "Don't you guys have one at your own detachment?"

Hall smiled. "I dunno, but I got a search warrant here that requires me to get one from this station."

"Believe me," Smyth said, cool as a cucumber, "if we had one, it 'ud be yours."

"Mind if I look around?" Hall asked as four more uniformed OPP officers walked through the front door.

*

By the way, did I mention Marion Kennedy? Marion was one of my clients at the CAS. Marion was about thirty-two. She had a three-year-old daughter named Melanie. Nice name, Melanie.

I received a page on my beeper one night I was on call. Being on staff with the CAS allows me to wear a beeper, just like a medical doctor or a plumber. I like it when it goes off at a concert or somewhere like that. . . . Is there a doctor in the house?

I arrived at Marion Kennedy's house at eleven-thirty in the evening. She was in a full-length, coffee- and housework-stained white terry bathrobe and fluffy pink nylon slippers. Marion held Melanie in her arms.

"Come in," said Marion.

"Thanks," I said, entering the living room of her one-bedroom apartment. The apartment was situated over Towne Waterbeds and Accessories. The living room had an old brown chesterfield, which, because of its sheer size, I gather came with the apartment. There were a couple of occasional chairs, also a brown coffee table with smoking paraphernalia and a twenty-four-inch colour TV.

The apartment smelled of poor people.

"Sit down," Marion said. I did.

Marion deposited Melanie on an orange cushion that sat in front of the TV. It was playing an old Rock Hudson movie. "I don't know what to do," said Marion.

"What's the problem?" I asked.

"I can't work," said Marion, "and I've got no money."

"Oh?" I said.

"Yeah," said Marion. "I had a job at the meat-packing plant, gutting turkeys."

"Good job?" I asked.

"The best," said Marion, "but I got hurt."

"On the job?" I asked.

"That's just the problem," said Marion. "I had finished my shift and was talking to some of the girls, and as I was leaving I slipped on a turkey giblet and fell on my back."

"Jeez," I said.

"Yeah," said Marion. Tears sprang to her eyes. "I buggered my back. I can't lift my arms up to gut," she sobbed. "I can't work."

I glanced over at Melanie. Melanie had fallen asleep as Rock Hudson embraced his leading lady. How appropriate, I thought.

"Sounds to me as if you qualify for workers' compensation," I said.

"They say the accident happened after I was off work. They say I can't qualify for workers' compensation. The accident has to happen on the job." Marion reached deep into her terry robe pocket and produced a used tissue.

"Do you have any unemployment benefits coming to you?"

"Yes," said Marion, "but they told me that I'm covered by workers' compensation. They won't give me any money unless I can show them I qualify."

"Jeez," I said. "How long do you figure you'll be off?"

"The chiropractor says maybe six weeks, maybe six months, maybe longer. He gave me this to wear," she said leaning forward and flipping a cervical collar from the floor towards me. The collar landed in my lap. "It seems to make it worse," Marion said.

"Look," I said, "I can get you emergency welfare payments at least until we get this mess straightened out."

"I can't clean the house. I can't wash the friggin' dishes, I can't sleep, I can't stand, and I can't sit."

"Jeez," I said.

"Look at her," Marion said, pointing to Melanie.

I did. Melanie was in a pink flannel nightie that was turning grey. She was a blond-headed little girl, thin, with dark circles under her eyes.

"I can't even take care of my daughter properly."

"Where's the dad?" I asked.

Marion looked at me as if I were from another planet.

"Where indeed," I mumbled to myself.

"I'm scared," said Marion. "I'm really scared. Sometimes I want to hit Melanie so hard when she starts to whine." Tears again rolled down her puffy cheeks. "I don't know what I can do. I'm scared, I'm depressed, and I don't know what to do. Sometimes I think I'm going to kill my daughter."

Marion struggled from her chair and went to her sleeping daughter. She knelt down beside her and softly stroked her sleeping daughter's thin blond hair.

"Do you hit her?" I asked softly.

"Not yet," said Marion.

"Do you want me to take her into care?" I asked.

"Not yet," said Marion.

*

At eight-thirty the next morning I arrived back at Marion Kennedy's apartment. I had a piece of paper in my hand that gave me the authority to pick up Melanie and take her into the care of the Children's Aid Society.

I knocked on the door. After a moment it was opened by Melanie. She was still in her grey-pink flannel nightie. "Your mom home?" I asked.

Melanie with the circles under her eyes didn't say anything. I walked into the apartment. Melanie was alone.

*

A week later I learned that Marion Kennedy had gone to Niagara Falls. Maybe she was looking for Melanie's dad, maybe she wasn't. I don't know. But whatever she went looking for, she didn't find it.

A newly married couple from Rochester stood pressed together at an observation platform downriver from the falls. They were looking at the morning mist. Below them, the young groom told the fire marshal, they saw Marion slip into the Niagara River. He said they saw her dog-paddling towards the falls. They said Marion appeared to be wearing some kind of collar.

*

Our visits to the marriage counsellor didn't seem to change anything, at least for me. If anything, I felt worse. Before I started the sessions, I had not been what you would call content. On the other hand, I hadn't been unhappy either.

Resentment, which did not exist before we started our weekly meetings, germinated and after the second session grew hourly.

Faith did little things, like trading in our four-door green 1969 Volvo on a silver 4-X-4 Jeep Cherokee. The odometer on our old green Volvo had been around the bend many times, but she had plenty of life still. When we were first married, Faith and I had excitedly collected flatware offered by a local supermarket as a premium. Faith replaced it with Jensen stainless steel.

My old psychology texts were suddenly off the bookshelves, replaced by current hardcover volumes from the Book-of-the-Month Club.

Our collection of records that we had listened to until they were worn thin ended up in a church flea market.

My old sweat-shirts, runners, wide ties, and seersucker suits were dropped into a Salvation Army box.

This was the little lady I had courted at university who had no thought beyond her next class suddenly making decisions that affected my life!

I'll tell you the truth: I thought we had a contract. I thought the contract said . . . this is what I am and this is what you are, and this is our dream.

Shall I tell you what our dream was? To remain true to who we were and what we believed in. . . . Is there anything wrong with that?

There seems to be fundamental breach of that agreement. Now Faith is sort of indicating that she wants to be me, or at least share being me. Where exactly does that leave yours truly?

Under the present state of the law, does that mean we have to renegotiate our contract or can I sue for breach? That's a question I wouldn't dare ask my present lawyer!

CHAPTER FIVE

MAGIC QUESTION NUMBER THREE:
Can you live with what you got? . . .

We were down to the wire now. It was session number nine. I was so agitated I don't even remember what our counsellor was wearing. Faith wore a cream Chanel suit with a white fleck in it. She had bought the ensemble on sale at Holt Renfrew in Toronto. I was wearing jeans and an old blue Levis shirt that I have had for as long as I can remember and a blue wool sweater that was only slightly older than the shirt. I loved that old sweater.

Faith seemed very relaxed, for Faith. She sat with her legs crossed. Her legs were covered in "nude" silk stockings. I think she wore cream pumps.

"This is the second last session," Faith began, "and I must say, I feel so much better. If nothing else, I've learned a lot about myself."

"Can you live with what you got?" I dared to ask.

Faith ignored my breach of the no-interruption rule.

"I feel as if I'm on the verge of something new and constructive."

"Can you live with what you got?" I asked again, only a little louder. Frankly, I was starting to panic.

Faith shifted in her chair and recrossed her legs. Faith has fantastic legs. Had I mentioned that? Very long. Tanned all year around and very shapely. Faith is a dark beauty, five feet, six inches, with dramatic black-brown eyes, a wide mouth, and ivory teeth that contrast with her dark perfect skin. It always gave me joy to look at her. . . . Could my dark beauty live with what she got? Could my gut await the answer?

Faith continued. "All my life I have lived with expectations, real and supposed. First my father's . . . that I would be a lady and not embarrass him, that he could point with pride to his little girl. That no disgrace would befall his good name. Then my mother . . . that I would be a good little girl, do what was expected, that I was 'capable,' and could do . . . fix, sew, cook, heal, soothe, make love, encourage, stand behind, and, like Betty Crocker, when the time was right, have a bun in the oven.

"And that was OK," she said. "That was OK. But now it's time to move on."

"Can you live with what you got?" I pleaded quietly to myself.

"I'm beginning to get a picture of who I am. Me." Faith went on. "I'm beginning to see that I can never fulfill other people's expectations of me, but that I can start to fulfill my own. I feel strong. I really do. I've even thought about children."

(Did you hear that? Children. Now. When she's good and ready.)

*

"Do you want to see a movie tonight?"
"Geez, honey, not really. Not tonight."

*

"Not my parents' grandchildren, but my children," Faith said.

(Sure, when you're ready, just let me know.)

*

"Do you want to see a movie tonight?"
"Not if it's going to be depressing like the last one."

*

"Professionally, I feel so strong too, so good about myself; I'm as good as any damn man, and better. I could burst."

(Where does that leave yours truly?)

*

"Do you want to see a movie tonight?"
"Which one?"

*

"I see myself. Clearly. I really do. And I like what I see. I like me."

Suddenly, involuntarily, I was on my feet. My throat burned. Tears ran down my cheeks. "DO YOU WANT TO SEE A MOVIE TONIGHT?" I screamed. "CAN YOU LIVE WITH WHAT YOU GOT?"

Both Faith and the counsellor looked at me. Saw me for the first time at that session. The counsellor fixed me with a kindly look and passed me a box of Kleenex. She looked at her watch and said, "I'm sorry. The hour's up."

*

I've ended up here at the hospital on the third floor, overlooking Lake Huron. I checked in the day before Faith and I were to have had our tenth and final session with our marriage counsellor. I think I need a bit of a rest. I think I take things too much to heart.

Faith's father wrote me a very nice note telling me to think more about myself and less about others.

That's kind of coincidence. That's exactly what Andrew Malcolm, my boss at the Children's Aid Society, said too, a few days before I checked in here. Andrew, who looks like an actor playing a quarterback for the Dallas Cowboys, is the director of the Children's Aid Society in this county. He is a very pragmatic fellow.

"If you were the father of those kids," Andrew said, "you wouldn't screw off and leave them. You haven't caused the problem, and you can't make it all better either."

"So what the heck am I doing?" I asked. "What am I getting paid for? . . . And while I'm at it, why does it always have to be women and children who bear the pain?"

"Look," said Andrew, "we need scapegoats. They make the rest of us feel good. You know what I mean? Someone worse off than us, someone to blame for high taxes, crummy housing, lousy work ethic, a shitty school system. We need 'em, boy," Andrew said, putting his arm around me and giving me a masculine kind of hug.

"Why does it have to be women and children who seem to shoulder society's need for a scapegoat?" I asked.

"Why?" Andrew said. "Simple. Men have made the rules, that's why!"

"Thanks," I said to my boss. "You make me feel a whole lot better."

"Don't mention it," Andrew said.

*

I'm having difficulty, too, with the third question that our counsellor required us to answer . . .

CHAPTER FIVE

MAGIC QUESTION NUMBER THREE:
Can you live with what you got?

I wonder, I really do. Can I live with what I got? Can I accept this bloody job? Can I accept the perks at someone else's expense? Can I accept the ugliness, the hypocrisy, the stupidity, the system made by men?

I wonder, too, if I can accept Faith. Can I accept the difference, the elusive difference? Can I accept the changes? Can I accept this new social system being created by women?

To tell you the truth, I dunno. I'm sick and I'm tired. I'm sick and tired of accepting anything.

A former teenage actor on stage and television, Paul Ross has worked as a magazine editor, a script writer, a political speechwriter, and as a reporter for the **Toronto Telegram**. Since 1969, he has practised law, including pioneer work in storefront law in Toronto's East End. In 1984, he was the subject of one of the legal profiles in Jack Batten's book, **Lawyers**.

Paul Ross now lives with his wife and two children near Goderich, Ontario where he practises law. He is presently at work on his next novel.

Printed in Canada